THE ILLINOIS RIVER

by JAMES AYARS

illustrated by Lili Réthi, (F.R.S.A.)

HOLT, RINEHART AND WINSTON
New York   Chicago   San Francisco

For Becky,

my severest and most helpful critic

ACKNOWLEDGMENTS

To the many persons, named or unnamed here, who helped me in my research for *The Illinois River* I express my sincere appreciation.

Members of the staff of the University of Illinois Library at Urbana cooperated in my search for published material. Dr. Robert Sutton and staff of the Illinois Historical Survey gave me access to rare publications on the early history of the river. Dr. Natalia M. Belting of the University of Illinois History Department generously directed me to valuable source material on the Indians and the French explorers. Dr. Milton D. Thompson and staff of the Illinois State Museum in Springfield provided information on Illinois Indians. Mrs. Lucretia S. Franklin of McNabb made available the unpublished diary of Eliza Wierman.

Through many years of pleasant association, Mr. Frank C. Bellrose and Dr. William C. Starrett, two of my fellow staff members of the Illinois Natural History Survey, contributed importantly to my knowledge and appreciation of the river. They read Chapter 14 for accuracy. Dr. R. Weldon Larimore, also a fellow staff member, and his son Richard accompanied me on the canoe cruise reported in Chapter 15.

Mr. Kenneth W. Stotler of Champaign and officials of Cargill, Inc., at Peoria arranged for my voyage on the towboat, the *Mark W. Rose,* described in Chapter 13. Officials of the Rose Barge Line generously provided me with passage on their towboat; Mr. Lloyd Eneix, Port Captain at Marseilles, introduced me to the crew of the towboat, gave me considerable information on towboating, and later read Chapter 13 for accuracy. Captain Oscar Elder extended to me the privileges of his boat. He, Pilot Ted Dean, and members of the crew courteously answered my innumerable questions about navigation and added to my appreciation of the river and the men who spend their lives on it.

Numerous residents of the cities and towns along the Illinois River helped in my understanding of the river and its people. The few I mention here must represent the many I should like to thank publicly: Miss Annabel Colvin, who was born in a cabin boat in the river at Kampsville and who, seventy years later, was living in the same structure drawn up on the south bank of the river at Beardstown; Miss Edith Keener of Naples, whose mother was the first woman to hold a pilot's license on the Illinois River and who, herself, once traveled the United States as a cowgirl in a Wild West show; Mr. and Mrs. Paul Vannier, who talk old days on the river with people who patronize their Boatel at Naples for gasoline, meals, or sleeping accommodations; Mr. Ross Dixon of Peoria, more than sixty years in the fish business, who remembers when Illinois River carp and buffalofish were shipped by the carload to New York and Boston; Mr. Henry C. Hart, for thirty-five years lockmaster at the Starved Rock Lock and Dam, who has seen water so high it was only a foot below the top of the lock walls; Father Martin Coughlin of St. Mary's Catholic Church at Utica, who thinks of his parish as a lineal descendant of the mission Father Jacques Marquette founded among the Kaskaskia Indians in 1675. The river is part of these people, and they are part of the river. Not to know them, or people like them, is not to know the river.

To Miss Ann Durell of Holt, Rinehart and Winston, I am grateful for the encouragement that started this book and for the patience that saw it finished. To Mrs. Edite Kroll and Mrs. Zay Borman I give thanks for helpful suggestions in revising the manuscript and for seeing it through the editorial mill.

To my wife, Rebecca Caudill, my dearest and severest critic, I express my appreciation publicly, as I often have privately, that during the writing of this book she never told me that what I wrote was good if she thought it wasn't. Without her encouragement and patient prodding, *The Illinois River* would still be in the planning stage.

JAMES AYARS

Urbana, Illinois
March 14, 1968

Contents

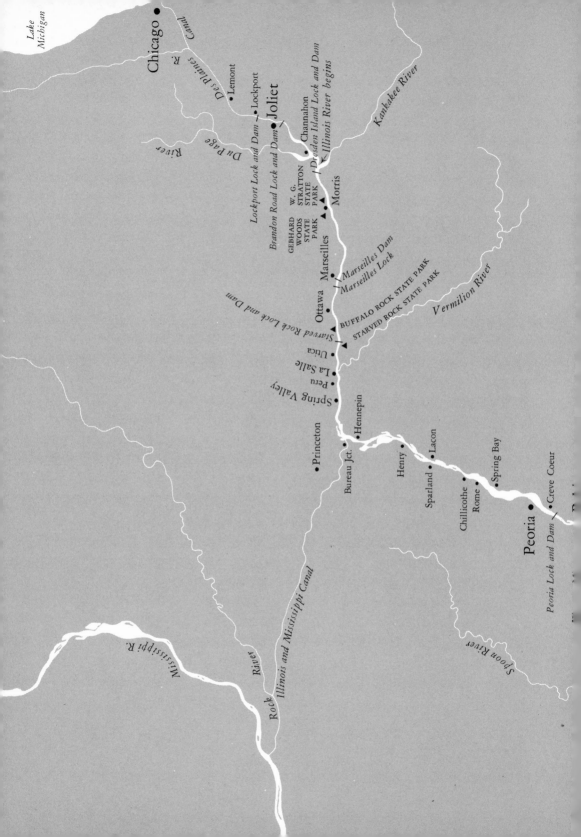

Lake
Michigan

Chicago

Des Plaines R.

Canal

Lemont

Lockport

Joliet

Lockport Lock and Dam

Du Page River

River

Brandon Road Lock and Dam

Channahon

Dresden Island Lock and Dam

Illinois River begins

Kankakee River

W. G.
STRATTON
STATE
PARK

GEBHARD
WOODS
STATE
PARK

Morris

Marseilles

Marseilles Dam

Marseilles Lock

Ottawa

BUFFALO ROCK STATE PARK

STARVED ROCK STATE PARK

Vermilion River

Starved Rock Lock and Dam

Utica

La Salle

Peru

Spring Valley

Princeton

Bureau Jct.

Hennepin

Henry

Lacon

Sparland

Chillicothe

Rome

Spring Bay

Creve Coeur

Peoria

Peoria Lock and Dam

Mississippi R.

Rock River

Illinois and Mississippi Canal

Spoon River

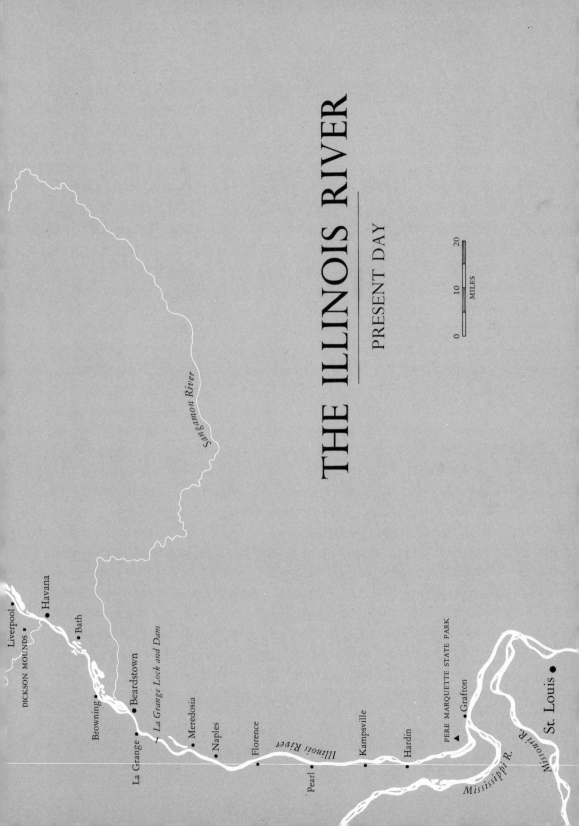

THE ILLINOIS RIVER

PRESENT DAY

0   10   20
MILES

Sangamon River

Illinois River

Mississippi R.

Missouri R.

Liverpool
Havana
DICKSON MOUNDS
Bath
Browning
Beardstown
La Grange Lock and Dam
La Grange
Meredosia
Naples
Florence
Pearl
Kampsville
Hardin
PERE MARQUETTE STATE PARK
Grafton
St. Louis

1.

How the River Came To Be

The Illinois River begins near Channahon, a small town with an Indian name meaning "the meeting of the waters," where the Des Plaines, flowing down from the northeast, joins the Kankakee, coming up from the southeast. It ends at Grafton, 275 miles downstream, where it flows out into the Mississippi River between a range of rocky, dome-shaped hills and a swampy area better known to ducks, horned owls, and muskrats than to men.

Compared to the Missouri, the Columbia, or the Tennessee, the Illinois is a short river. Its importance is not in its length or lack of length, but in its place on the map of North America, its place in time, its place in the economy of a wealthy nation.

As the river winds its leisurely way through a fertile land, it flows past modernized homes, mechanized farms, computerized offices and factories. Beneath its quiet waters, beneath the cities and farms of its broad valley, sleep millions of years of geologic time. From layers of rock that lie beneath the fertile land, geologists have been able to read the history of those years.

Half a billion years ago, in a time geologists call the Cambrian Period, a shallow salt sea lay over all of the flat Illinois country—that part of the earth's surface now known as the state of Illinois. Fossils of trilobites and brachiopods found in layers of rock show that in this period life in the sea had begun. Then one day the earth rumbled and quaked. Land rose out of the water, and the sea retreated.

Several times in later eons, the sea returned to the Illinois country, covered it for millions of years, and retreated toward the south. Each time water covered the land for a long period, one or more layers of rock were formed from small particles that had settled at the bottom of the sea. Shale and sandstone were formed from particles of older rock that had been broken up by water or frost. Limestone was formed from the shells of small animals that had lived and died in the sea. How many millions of years ago the oldest of these layers or strata of rock were laid down can be known by measuring the radioactivity of certain elements in the rock.

The parade of animal life that began in the Cambrian Period continued as time rolled slowly on. In a period sometimes known as the Age of Fishes, the sea teemed with animal life. Perhaps the sea did not have room for all the life in it; some animals, and some plants, too, moved from the water to live on land. The two periods that followed the Age of Fishes, the Mississippian and the Pennsylvanian, are of special importance. They provided the bedrock (the rock nearest the surface) for most of the Illinois River valley: the Mississippian for the lower part and the Pennsylvanian for the upper. Stored in the earth during these periods was great wealth, most of it within the reach of modern man.

In the Mississippian Period, the sea moved in and out of the Illinois country several times, leaving deposits that became shale, sandstone, or limestone. Over a large area a few miles south of the present Illinois River, where enormous numbers of plants and animals lived and died, oil was formed. The parade of animals in this period included salamander-like amphibians, animals that spent parts of their lives in water, but most of it on land.

In the Pennsylvanian Period, about 225 million years ago, ridges or small mountains were created by folding of the earth's surface. The climate of this period, like periods before it, was moist and warm. In

2

vast swamps between the ridges, giant fernlike trees and other plants grew in great abundance, died, and formed beds of peat that eventually, under the pressure of later deposits, became coal.

Layers of coal, shale, sandstone, and limestone tell the story of animal life in the Pennsylvanian Period. In the water, on land, in the air, countless numbers of animals swam, waddled, or flew. Dragonflies with wingspreads of more than two feet glided between giant fernlike trees in the swamps. Cockroaches, some of them much larger than any now known, were so numerous that the period has sometimes been called the Age of Cockroaches. Toward the end of the Pennsylvanian Period, reptiles appeared in the parade. Unlike all other animals before them, they were entirely adapted to living on land.

For about 2 million years after the end of the Pennsylvanian Period, time left little or no record in the Illinois country. All of the area except for a small part at the southern tip was above water. Where no water covered the land, no layers of rock were formed to preserve as fossils the plants and animals of the period.

In the rock of nearby areas have been found the remains of dinosaurs sixty-five feet long, flying reptiles that may have been ancestors of the birds, small horses that ran on their middle toes, beavers, squirrels, mice, camels, cats, wolflike dogs, and many other animals. Undoubtedly, these animals were in the Illinois country also.

About a million years ago, temperatures in the Illinois country gradually dropped. To the north, immense ice sheets, or glaciers, covered the land from ocean to ocean. As the ice sheets grew larger, they pushed out in all directions.

The cause of the Glacial Period, or Ice Age, has puzzled scientists for many years. Geologists have suggested several possible causes, such as shifting of the earth on its axis, less carbon dioxide in the air, unusual sunspots.

Four times during the Glacial Period ice sheets invaded the Illinois

3

country from the north as the seas had invaded it from the south. And each time the ice ground its slow way over the surface it changed the face of the land.

Each of the four great invasions of ice was made up of several advances and retreats. As an ice sheet moved southward, like a gigantic bulldozer it leveled the land over which it passed. Some of the rock and soil it pushed ahead of it. Some it picked up and carried along with it. When the ice melted back, it left its loads as glacial drift—clay, sand, and gravel, with rocks of various sizes. The Great Lakes were scooped out by ice sheets, and ancient lakes that were larger than the largest of these formed behind ridges of glacial drift.

Times of the melting away of the glaciers were periods of great water activity. Running water is both a wearer away and a sorter of rock material. A swift stream of water carrying with it a variety of rock material drops first its heaviest objects and finally its lightest. Rich deposits of gravel and sand now found along the Illinois River were left there by water that flowed from melting glaciers.

The most important of the glacial invasions in making the Illinois River valley what it is today were the third and fourth.

In the third invasion, called the Illinoian, ice moved down from the northeast and covered all of the Illinois country except for small areas on the northern, western, and southern edges. When the ice melted away, probably less than two hundred fifty thousand years ago, it left enormous quantities of glacial drift over the bedrock.

In the fourth invasion, called the Wisconsinan, ice moved down from the northeast, as it had before, and covered a third of the Illinois country—the northeastern third. When the ice melted away, about ten thousand years ago, Wisconsinan drift covered part of the Illinoian drift. From the Illinoian drift has been formed much of the soil along the lower part of the Illinois River and from the Wisconsinan drift much of the soil along the upper part. Younger than the Illinoian soil,

Ancient river created by meltwater from glaciers.

the Wisconsinan has had less of its limestone and other plant nutrients leached away and so is more fertile.

Invasions of the glaciers, invasions of the seas, into the Illinois country are of interest not only to geologists. Events of ten thousand years ago—of 200 million years ago—have shaped life along the Illinois River today.

The seas and the glaciers divided the Illinois River into an upper part and a lower part, a younger part and an older part. From its beginning near Channahon to the sweeping southward bend near Hennepin, the river flows with little wandering through a valley about one and a half miles wide. Below the bend, the river, as if suddenly grown both old and tired, meanders aimlessly in a floodplain two to five miles wide. Before the days of dams on the Illinois, the upper river, from Channahon to Hennepin, fell 50 feet in 63 miles, the lower river only 25 feet in 215 miles. Too swift for early steamboats, the upper river held promise for the development of waterpower, and many sawmills and gristmills were built by settlers along its tributaries. Too slow to be a source of waterpower, the lower river was useful as a waterway, and many of the early Illinois settlers came into the state on steamboats that chugged up river as far as Beardstown and Peoria.

Lavishly generous were the seas and the glaciers that invaded the Illinois country long ago. They come alive today in the wealth of the area. Limestone from the shells of tiny animals brought in by salt seas from the south has gone into crops of corn and soybeans, concrete roads, houses, office buildings, factories. Coal from fernlike trees that grew luxuriantly in boggy areas after the seas receded has become heat for comfort and light for learning. Grains of sand laid down by glacial streams have become the windows of homes, office buildings, and factories; the lenses of eyeglasses, binoculars, and microscopes.

Prelude to History

The first families of man to live in the Illinois country probably arrived before the last glaciers had left. Scientists believe they wandered into the area from the north or west, following herds of big animals they hunted for food.

Who were the first families of the Illinois country? Where had they come from? The answers to these questions depend upon the answer to another: Who were the American Indians?

For many years, archeologists, those scientists who study the history of ancient man, puzzled over this question. They observed that the American Indians looked much like the Mongoloid peoples of eastern Asia in color of skin and shape of head. They compared the heads of men who lived long ago in North America with the heads of men who lived long ago in Asia and found them similar. They noted how near Alaska is to Siberia. Most of them came to the conclusion that the Indians were descendants of people who had migrated to North America from Asia thousands of years ago.

Perhaps those people of long ago crossed on a land bridge between Siberia and Alaska—a bridge that may have existed one or more times in the ancient past. Perhaps they walked across on ice. Perhaps they paddled the fifty-six miles that separate Asia and North America at Bering Strait; they may have done some island hopping, for three islands lie in the strait, and the greatest distance of open water is only twenty-five miles.

Having arrived in North America, those ancient people moved southward and eastward, perhaps in corridors between advancing or retreating glaciers of the Ice Age. Large flint spearheads found with the bones of prehistoric animals lead archeologists to believe that the first men in North America were hunters of big mammals, that they obtained at least part of their food from such cold-weather animals as the mammoth and the musk ox, and that some of them followed herds of those animals until they arrived in the Illinois country. Spearheads believed to have been used eight thousand to twelve thousand years ago have been found on the Illinois prairies.

As the climate of the Illinois country became warmer and the glaciers melted back, the big animals moved north. Some of the hunters and their families followed. Others remained. They or their descendants left refuse piles, burial mounds, and ruined villages that have been covered for many centuries.

Just as geologists read the history of the earth from layers of rock and soil, archeologists read the history of ancient man from layers, or strata, of buried past. Such simple objects as grains of corn, bones of deer, clam shells, chipped stones, charred wood, or bits of broken pots, when found in layers of soil, become letters and words that archeologists put together in writing the history of man in the ancient past.

Archeologists have been helped in their study of ancient peoples by radiocarbon dating, a technique discovered in 1946. By this technique, they can estimate the age of each layer of buried past containing the remains of things that once lived.

The oldest known human habitation in the Illinois country is the Modoc Rock Shelter, about three miles from the Mississippi River and less than one hundred miles by water below the mouth of the Illinois. Archeologists first learned of the shelter in 1952. A crew of workmen digging in the soil along the highway between Modoc and Prairie du

Rocher had turned up a large number of bones and spearheads beneath the overhang of a sandstone bluff.

In layers of soil, for a depth of twenty-eight feet, the archeologists found stone axes, hammers, spearheads, and other tools and weapons, pieces of pottery, bones of deer and turkeys, shells of turtles and mussels, copper jewelry, seeds of plants, and many other items that had once been part of life in the shelter. They found carefully buried skeletons of men, women, and children, people who had once used the tools, weapons, and pottery, had worn the jewelry, had tossed aside the bones of deer and turkeys after gnawing off the meat. Each item the archeologists labeled, noting the stratum, or layer of soil, from which it came. In their twenty-eight feet of digging, they uncovered ten thousand years of buried past. By studying items in the various strata from the lowest to the highest, they were able to picture how people lived at almost any time in a hundred centuries and to view civilization in the making.

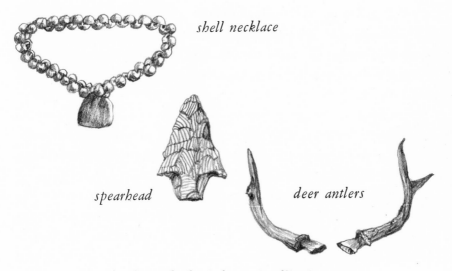

shell necklace

spearhead   *deer antlers*

Articles from the buried past in Illinois country.

No human habitation as old as the Modoc Rock Shelter has been found along the Illinois River. But Modoc is not more than two hundred miles overland from the present-day Peoria, which is about midway of the Illinois. And, ten thousand years ago, life along the Illinois must have been much like life along the Mississippi at Modoc.

Although the first families of the Illinois country were only hunters and collectors of food, later families learned to store food, principally nuts and acorns. They invented new weapons and tools and improved the old. Still later families learned to cultivate plants that supplied them with food. Food became more abundant or easier to get. People had more time to fashion ornaments from the bones or teeth of wild animals, or from the shells of mussels, to wear around their necks and make themselves beautiful. They had time to bury their dead with considerable ceremony. (The graves of people buried more than six thousand years ago have been found in the Modoc Rock Shelter.) Also, they had time to tame wolves or coyotes, some of which they buried with members of their families.

About the time Julius Caesar and his Roman legions were forcing civilization on the savages in Britain and St. Patrick was taking Christianity to the heathen Irish, a golden age of culture was flourishing in the Illinois country and nearby parts of North America. It lasted approximately a thousand years, about half of it before the birth of Jesus of Nazareth and about half of it afterward. It was known as the Hopewellian Period.

That it was a period of food abundance and leisure time is shown by the artifacts found with skeletons in burial mounds or graves of the period—bone ornaments with delicate designs etched on them, beautifully decorated pottery, hammered copper jewelry, skillfully fashioned pipes of stone and statuettes of clay. People required to spend most of their days gathering food to keep themselves alive would have had no time for making such items of luxury.

Vases and a carved stone pipe from Illinois River sites.

That it was a comparatively peaceful period is indicated by the materials that came from distant places—copper from the Lake Superior region, pipestone from Ohio, small shells from the South Atlantic and Gulf coasts, and a black stone, obsidian, from Mexico or the Yellowstone. Only a period of peace would have allowed the wide travel needed to bring these items from distant places.

The Hopewellians were remarkable because they developed a high degree of culture without the domestic animals possessed at that time by the savages in Britain. They had no horses, cows, sheep, hogs, or poultry. They had only the dog, a tamed wolf or coyote. But they had, probably for the first time in their part of North America, a plant not known in Britain—or in Europe or Asia. They had maize, or Indian corn.

Brought from Mexico or Central America, this corn found the soil and climate of the Illinois country much to its liking. Cultivated by the Hopewellians, it rewarded them with an abundance of food in exchange for little effort—much less effort than was required for living on animals that had to be hunted and killed, or on wild plant food that had to be collected from the forests and prairies.

The Hopewellians had time to build substantial dwellings, both four-sided and circular. They had time to make beautiful pottery, jewelry, and feather-cloth robes. They also had time, archeologists believe, to develop a formal religion with elaborate ceremonies presided over by priests. A study of artifacts indicates that the Hopewellian Period was brighter for some individuals, possibly those of the priest class, than for others. Certainly, the burial mounds reveal, a privileged class or classes developed in the society.

The bright Hopewellian Period was followed in the Illinois country by a dark age. The villages became smaller, the dwellings less substantial, the tools, weapons, pottery, and jewelry less carefully made. The reason for the dark age is not known, but it lasted until about 1000 A.D.

Then, about the time William of Normandy was directing his archers at the Battle of Hastings to aim their arrows upward and let them fall in the faces of the Saxons, the people of the Illinois country were learning to use the bow and arrow. Possibly the new weapon, which could be shot fast and often, possibly a long period of favorable weather, helped to lift these people out of the dark age.

Trade and travel increased. Dwellings once more became substantial; many were made with rectangular floors and with walls of vertical posts interlaced with branches and twigs plastered with clay. Evidently food became more plentiful. Possibly beans and squash were added to the corn and other plants previously cultivated. For approximately five hundred years, until about the time Columbus discovered the New World, people of the Illinois country enjoyed a prosperous period almost like that of the Hopewellian.

When white men first heard of the Illinois country, the people living there belonged to a nation of Indians called the Iliniwek, Ilini, or Ilinois (later spelled Illinois). Their homeland was bounded by four rivers—the Wisconsin, the Mississippi, the Ohio, the Wabash—and Lake Michigan, then called the Lake of the Illinois. In this fertile territory, much of it drained by the Illinois River, lived the Kaskaskia, Peoria, Tamaroa, Cahokia, and other tribes that were members of the Iliniwek.

In the native language, "Iliniwek" was the word for "the men." It was used in a way that implied all other Indians were somewhat less than men.

In 1655, a small band of Iroquois Indians, living many miles to the east, went on a long warpath, attacked a village of the Iliniwek when the men were away from home, and killed the women and children. The Iliniwek assembled their warriors, attacked the invaders, and defeated them. This incident was the beginning of a costly war that lasted twelve years.

Not only did the Iliniwek carry on the long war with the distant Iroquois; they battled almost constantly with the fierce Sioux, their near neighbors to the north and west, and occasionally with the Winnebagos to the north. By the time white men entered the Illinois country, the Iliniwek had been severely weakened by war. Many of their young warriors had been killed in battle or taken as slaves. As a nation, the Iliniwek were no longer "the men."

3.

Prelude to Discovery

Historians do not know for certain the names of the first white men to see the country of the Iliniwek and the Illinois River. In an age of exploration—the second half of the seventeenth century—hardy adventurers fanned out westward, deep into the wilderness, from tiny French settlements along the St. Lawrence River. *Coureurs de bois* most of them were—woods runners—men seeking adventure, fortune, or merely subsistence in the hard commerce of the fur trade. They lived for the lusty present and had little sense of history. Most of them had little or no book learning. Because they could not or would not write, they left no permanent records. But sometimes, when well-known explorers pushed into uncharted wilderness, they found evidence that other white men, nameless to history, had been there before them.

Even though historians are not certain about the first white men to see the Illinois, most of them name the Sieur Louis Jolliet and Father Jacques Marquette as the discoverers of the river. They acknowledge that Jolliet and Marquette guided their bark canoes into the quiet waters of the Illinois while returning from their exploration of another river, the great river called by the natives the Mississippi. They recognize that these Frenchmen were the first to come out of the wilderness and make the Illinois River known to the world.

Almost two centuries had passed since Columbus sighted the New World, more than half a century since Captain John Smith pointed his pistol at Chief Powhatan's braves and Samuel de Champlain terrified the Iroquois Indians with blasts from his blunderbusses. The French and the English were in the New World, both striving to make it their own. Both were engaged in a great westward movement. In the mainstream of that movement were Jolliet and Marquette.

The French were seeking to increase the size of their territory; strengthen their colony; hem in the English on the Atlantic seaboard; extend their profitable fur trade; find copper, gold, silver, and lead; discover a new way to the Orient; and convert the natives to the Christian religion.

"As after the increase of the colony, there is nothing more important for the colony than the discovery of a passage to the south sea, his majesty wishes you to give it your attention," the colonial minister of the French King Louis XIV wrote to Jean Baptiste Talon, the King's Intendant at Quebec.

Intendant Talon gave it his attention, as his majesty had wished, and a few months later the Count de Frontenac, newly arrived Governor of the province, sent a letter to the King's colonial minister.

"M. Talon has . . . judged it expedient for the service," Governor Frontenac wrote, "to send the sieur Jolliet to discover the South sea by the country of the Maskoutens and the great river called the Mississipi, which is believed to discharge into the Californie sea. He is a man very skillful in this kind of discovery and has already been near the great river, of which he promises to discover the mouth."

Even before Governor Frontenac wrote these words, the Sieur Jolliet with a few hardy voyageurs in a birchbark canoe had set out from Quebec toward the west. Up the St. Lawrence he paddled, up the swift Ottawa River, across Lake Nipissing, down the French River, along the northern rim of Georgian Bay, to Michilimackinac, the region of water and land where Lake Michigan and Lake Huron meet. With him he carried instructions from Father Claude Dablon, superior of the missions of the Jesuit order in New France, that Father Jacques

15

Sieur Louis Jolliet, co-discoverer of the Illinois River.

Marquette should accompany him on his exploration of the Mississippi. At the mission of St. Ignace (where St. Ignace, Michigan, is now), Jolliet found Marquette.

Louis Jolliet had been born in the riverside village of Quebec twenty-five years after a small ship named the Mayflower had landed a cargo of Englishmen at Plymouth Rock. Son of a poor wagon-maker in the employ of a fur-trading company, he had studied for the priesthood and had taken some of the vows of the Jesuit order.

At the age of twenty-three he set about perfecting the skills then needed by a young man who hoped for success as an explorer. By the time he was twenty-eight, when he and Marquette were chosen to find and explore the Mississippi, he was "considered very fit for so great an enterprise."

He had mastered wilderness craft—canoeing, hunting, fishing, cooking in the open, building shelter huts, reading and making maps, finding his way in the darkest forests.

His ability was known to the Governor and the Intendant at Quebec.

"They were not mistaken," wrote Father Dablon, "in the choice that they made of Sieur Jolyet, For he is a young man, born in this country, who possesses all the qualifications that could be desired for such an undertaking. He has experience and Knows the Languages spoken in the Country of the Outaouacs [Ottawas], where he has passed several years. He possesses Tact and prudence, which are the chief qualities necessary for the success of a voyage as dangerous as it is difficult. Finally, he has the Courage to dread nothing where everything is to be Feared."

Jacques Marquette was eight years older than Jolliet. Born in France, he was a member of a prominent family that had lived for many generations in the ancient walled city of Laon. At seventeen, he entered a Jesuit college. For several years, he lived the life of a sincere scholar, kindly priest, and gentle teacher in his native land. But, as he read the records of Jesuit missionaries among the American Indians, he longed to serve his order in the New World. At the age of twenty-nine, he was sent to New France to become a forest missionary. After "a somewhat prolonged voyage"—probably of three or four months—he arrived at Quebec on September 20, 1666.

Although not physically rugged, Marquette subjected himself to all the hardships of long wilderness journeys—hard labor at the paddle and on the overland portage, cold, hunger, dirt, disease, pestilential insects, and the danger of attack from enemy tribes of Indians.

"You should love the Indians like brothers, with whom you are to spend the rest of your life," advised the writer of a circular issued in France by the Jesuits to members of their order going to the New World as forest missionaries. "Never make them wait for you in embarking.—Take a flint and steel to light their pipes and kindle their fire at night; for these little services win their hearts.—Try to eat their sagamité [cornmeal boiled in water and seasoned with fat] as they cook it, bad and dirty as it is.—Fasten up the skirts of your cassock, that you may not carry water or sand into the canoe.—Wear no shoes or stockings in the canoe; but you may put them on in crossing the portages.—Do not make yourself troublesome, even to a single Indian.—Do not ask them too many questions.—Bear their faults in silence, and appear always cheerful.—Buy fish for them from the tribes you will pass; and for this purpose take with you some awls, beads, knives, and fish-hooks.—Be not ceremonious with the Indians; take at once what they offer you: ceremony offends them.—Be very careful, when in the canoe, that the brim of your hat does not annoy them. Perhaps it would be better to wear your night-cap. There is no such thing as impropriety among Indians.—Remember that it is Christ and his cross that you are seeking; and if you aim at anything else, you will get nothing but affliction for body and mind."

In less than two years after arriving in New France, Marquette was ready for an important assignment. In the journal kept by the Jesuits at Quebec was written this entry for April 21, 1668: "Father Marquette, two men, and a young lad await an opportunity of going to the Outawak [Ottawa] country."

The opportunity for which Marquette waited was passage with a party of Indians or of fur-traders returning to the Ottawa country from a visit to the settlements along the St. Lawrence. Many leagues to the west, at Sault de Ste. Marie, between Lake Huron and Lake Superior, waited the Jesuit mission to which he was assigned.

At the mission, Marquette found Indians of many tribes camped in the clearings, most of them there for the atticameg, or white fish, they netted from the swift river. Ottawas were there, and Crees, Menominees, Potawatomis, Sacs, Foxes, Winnebagos, and Miamis—twenty or thirty nations, all differing in language, customs, and politics. There, too, were Indians of the nation known as the Iliniwek or Illinois.

Marquette was at the Sault only a year when he was ordered farther west, to a lonely mission, La Pointe du St. Esprit (Point of the Holy

Father Jacques Marquette, forest missionary and explorer.

Spirit), at the southwest corner of Lake Superior. There he would be the only missionary, the head of the mission. As soon as another missionary could be found to take over his duties at La Pointe, he would be sent to establish a mission among the Illinois. Rejoicing in his new assignment, he set out with a few Frenchmen and Indians on an arduous voyage of 500 miles.

Wintry weather came early in the northern country that year. Marquette and his party arrived in their frail canoes at La Pointe in the middle of September, 1669, "after a Voyage of a month . . . amid almost constant dangers of death."

At La Pointe, Marquette found Hurons, Ottawas, and Indians of other tribes camped in the clearings. In the cold waters of Chequamegon Bay, the Indians found a plentiful supply of fish and, in the swamps south of the bay, relative safety from the bloodthirsty Iroquois of the east and the fierce Nadouessi (Sioux) of the west. At the time of Marquette's arrival, they were enjoying a long period of peace.

Although some of the Indians at La Pointe possessed "a little Christianity," others were "very far from the Kingdom of God," Father Marquette reported in a letter to his superior, Father François le Mercier. "They turn Prayer to ridicule, and scarcely will they hear us speak of Christianity; they are proud and without intelligence." Among such Indians, Marquette could do little more than baptize the sick, the dying, and the children too young to protest.

The Illinois Indians who visited the mission appeared to be different. Although they worshiped the sun and thunder, they were "fairly well inclined toward Christianity." They even urged Marquette to come to teach them in their country, which was "distant from la pointe thirty days' journey by land, by a very difficult route."

They were a nation of warriors and in battle took many captives, which they held as slaves. Some of their slaves they sold to the Ottawas for muskets, gunpowder, kettles, hatchets, and knives.

"Those whom I have seen," Marquette wrote of the Illinois, "seem to be of a tolerably good disposition . . . and they promise me to embrace Christianity, and observe all that I shall say." He added: "They believe that, if I go to them, I shall establish peace everywhere."

From the Illinois Indians, Marquette heard accounts of the Mississippi, the river that was to make him more famous as an explorer than as a priest.

"When the Ilinois come to la Pointe," he wrote, "they cross a great river which is nearly a league [about two and three-quarters miles] in width, flows from North to South, and to such a distance that the Ilinois, who do not know what a Canoe is, have not yet heard any mention of its mouth. . . . It is hard to believe that that great River discharges its waters in Virginia, and we think rather that it has its mouth in California."

Marquette was no more ignorant of geography than other men of his time. No white man knew the course of the Mississippi, for no white man had explored its entire length.

As Marquette went daily among the Indians at La Pointe, preaching to them, talking with them, he developed a yearning to see the great river to the south—a yearning that was joined to a strong desire to establish a mission among the Illinois.

Then, suddenly, in the second year at La Pointe, Marquette's thoughts of the river and the mission among the Illinois were interrupted. The long period of peace between the Sioux and the Indians at La Pointe was broken. Quarrels had been followed by murders.

Marquette tried to restore peace. He sent presents—religious pictures—to the Sioux. Scornfully, but with dignity, the Sioux returned the presents and declared war upon the Indians at La Pointe.

What should the Indians at the mission do in this ominous spring of 1671? Their bark houses rimmed the sparkling blue waters of Chequamegon Bay. The fields in which they grew their corn and pumpkins lay nearby. Wild berries grew in the clearings, wild rice in the streams. Fish were abundant in the lake and could be had for the taking.

In a spirit of unusual magnanimity, the fierce Sioux delayed their attack, allowing their enemies time to hold councils and come to a decision.

Sadly the tribes at La Pointe decided to leave this land of plenty. The Hurons decided to return to Michilimackinac. Some of the Ottawas decided to return to Michilimackinac, others to their old home on an island in Lake Huron. They loaded their stores of dried food and cooking utensils, their clothes, tools, and weapons into birchbark canoes and pushed off on the rugged voyage of more than five hundred miles. With the Hurons went Father Marquette.

To Jacques Marquette, heading eastward, the great river to the south and the mission he hoped to establish among the Illinois must have seemed very far away.

4.

"We Have Seen Nothing Like This River"

Weary but safely arrived at Michilimackinac, Father Jacques Marquette settled down at the mission of St. Ignace. As he worked among the Hurons there, he thought of the great river to the southwest and of the Illinois Indians who at La Pointe had urged him to come to them.

Then, early in December, 1672, Louis Jolliet arrived from Quebec with news that the Jesuit priest was to accompany him on a voyage of exploration of the Mississippi River.

Exactly what Jolliet and Marquette wrote in the journals they kept of that long voyage historians can only guess. When Jolliet, who had "passed through a thousand dangers," was on his way back to Quebec, his canoe upset in the last rapid of the St. Lawrence River above Montreal. He "lost both his men and his papers" and "escaped only by a sort of Miracle." Marquette's journal disappeared soon after the voyage was completed. His map still exists. From this map, from a map made by Jolliet about a year after the voyage was ended, from Jolliet's brief writings, from a long report written by Father Dablon, and from a letter written by Father Dablon after talking with Jolliet, historians have been able to learn about the voyage.

Father Dablon's long report was written as if it had been narrated by Marquette, and for more than two hundred years it was believed to be Marquette's journal. It is referred to in this chapter as the Narra-

Winter camp of missionaries and Indians.

tive and the person reporting as the Narrator. Although it undoubtedly contains some inaccuracies, and may contain details supplied by Father Dablon from his own knowledge of Indians, it is the best account of the voyage now available.

The elation Marquette felt at the news Jolliet had brought from Quebec is plainly revealed in the Narrative:

"I was all the more delighted at This good news, since I saw that my plans were about to be accomplished; and since I found myself in the blessed necessity of exposing my life for the salvation of all these peoples, and especially of the Ilinois, who had very urgently entreated me, when I was at la pointe du st. Esprit, to carry the word of God to Their country."

The two men, the skilled explorer and the dedicated priest, had met and become good friends in Quebec six years before. Now they spent many days during the winter preparing for their journey and waiting for the break-up of ice in the lakes and rivers.

"And because We were going to seek Unknown countries," the Narrator relates, "We took every precaution in our power, so that, if our Undertaking were hazardous, it should not be foolhardy."

From Indians who lived or hunted in the country to the south and west, Jolliet and Marquette collected as much information as possible about the region they hoped to explore. With this information and their knowledge of geography, they constructed a map. On it they traced the courses of the rivers they planned to navigate, the names and the territories of the Indian tribes they thought they would meet, and the imagined course of the great river that was the object of their search.

"We were not long in preparing all our Equipment," the Narrator states, "although we were about to Begin a voyage, the duration of which we could not foresee." Indian corn and smoked meat were the only provisions.

In the middle of May, 1673, the exploring party—Jolliet, Marquette, and five other Frenchmen—set out in two birchbark canoes from the mission of St. Ignace, "fully resolved to do and suffer everything for so glorious an Undertaking."

In the words of the Narrative: "The Joy we felt at being selected for This Expedition animated our Courage, and rendered the labor of paddling from morning to night agreeable to us."

Along the northern shore of Lake Michigan, Jolliet, Marquette, and their companions "Joyfully Plied" their paddles and into the Baye des Puans (now Green Bay). On the west shore of the bay, dark green with dense forests of pine and tamarack, lived friendly Indians who advised them to give up their plans to explore the Mississippi because along its banks were tribes that "never show Mercy to Strangers, but Break Their heads without cause."

Marquette appreciated the advice but, he said, he could not follow it, "because the salvation of souls was at stake," and for this he would be "delighted" to give his life. At the lower end of the bay, the explorers found a river (now known as the Fox), very beautiful and flowing gently at its mouth. As the Frenchmen headed their canoes into the river and moved upstream, flocks of ducks and geese flew up from the beds of wild rice growing in the water. The gentle flow at the mouth of the river soon gave way to a rapid with a current too swift to paddle against and with rocks so sharp they cut the bark canoes and the feet of the men trying to drag their craft upstream. Beside the rapid, known as De Pere (site of De Pere, Wisconsin), clustered the bark chapel and other rude buildings of the Jesuit mission of St. François Xavier.

Four more rapids and several miles of hard paddling brought the seven Frenchmen to the palisaded village known as Mascoutens. Three weeks had passed since the explorers left Michilimackinac and they had now reached "the limit of the discoveries which the french have made."

Indians of three nations had gathered at the village—Miamis, Mascoutens, and Kikabous (Kickapoos).

"No sooner had we arrived," the Narrator states, "than we, Monsieur Jollyet and I, assembled the elders together; and he told them that he was sent by Monsieur Our Governor to discover New countries, while I was sent by God to Illumine them with the light of the holy Gospel."

At no great distance from the village, Jolliet knew, was a river called the Meskousing (now the Wisconsin) that flowed into the Mississippi. But between lay a maze of swamp, lake, and stream. In exchange for a present, the Indians promised guides. Then they gave their guests a mat to be used as a bed throughout the voyage.

On the following day, the explorers, with two Miamis, embarked "in the sight of a great crowd, who could not sufficiently express their astonishment at the sight of seven frenchmen, alone and in two Canoes, daring to undertake so extraordinary and so hazardous an Expedition."

Through the water maze the Miamis guided the Frenchmen to a place only twenty-seven hundred paces from the Meskousing (near the site of Portage, Wisconsin). There they helped to portage the canoes from the eastward-flowing Fox to the westward-flowing Meskousing, "after which," says the Narrator, "they returned home, leaving us alone in this Unknown country, in the hands of providence."

Down the Meskousing, "full of Islands Covered with Vines," the Frenchmen paddled. The sandy bottom formed shoals that made navigation difficult.

"After proceeding 40 leagues [about 110 miles] on This same route," the Narrator records, "We arrived at the mouth of our River; and, at 42 and a half degrees Of latitude, We safely entered Missisipi on The 17th of June, with a Joy that I cannot Express." (The actual date may have been June 15.) Paddling downstream, the explorers found that the river alternately widened and narrowed, that the land through which it flowed varied from wooded hills to flat prairies.

"From time to time," says the Narrator, "we came upon monstrous fish, one of which struck our Canoe with such violence that I Thought that it was a great tree, about to break the Canoe to pieces. On another occasion, we saw on The water a monster with the head of a tiger, a sharp nose Like That of a wildcat, with whiskers and straight, Erect ears; The head was gray and The Neck quite black; but We saw no more creatures of this sort."

Along the shore, the Frenchmen saw "wild cattle" (bison or buffalo) as many as four hundred in a herd.

Advancing into unknown country, they kept always on their guard. Toward evening of each day, they landed and made a small fire to cook their food. At night, they slept in their canoes anchored in the river some distance from shore.

For a week they paddled and sailed downstream, covering sixty leagues (about 165 miles) and seeing many birds and four-footed animals, but no Indians, friendly or unfriendly.

"Finally, on the 25th of June," the Narrator records, "we perceived on the water's edge some tracks of men, and a narrow and somewhat beaten path leading to a beautiful prairie. We stopped to Examine it; and, thinking that it was a road that Led to some village of savages, We resolved to go and reconnoiter it. We therefore left our two Canoes under the guard of our men, strictly charging Them not to allow themselves to be surprised, after which Monsieur Jollyet and I undertook this investigation—a rather hazardous one for two men who exposed themselves, alone, to the mercy of a barbarous and Unknown people. We silently followed The narrow path, and, after walking About 2 leagues [about five and a half miles], We discovered a village on the bank of the river [probably the river now known as the Iowa], and two others on a Hill distant about a league from the first. Then we Heartily commended ourselves to God, and, after imploring his aid, we went farther without being perceived, and approached so near that we could even hear the savages talking. We therefore Decided that it was time to reveal ourselves. This We did by Shouting with all Our energy, and stopped without advancing any farther."

At the sound of shouting, Indians swarmed out of their lodges and stared at the strangers. They knew from the black gown worn by Marquette that the strangers were Frenchmen and therefore probably friends. Perhaps they saw no reason to distrust two visitors who had so openly announced their approach.

For a few minutes, the Indians held counsel. Then from the group emerged four old men, walking slowly and in silence toward the two Frenchmen.

Two of the old men carried calumets, ceremonial tobacco pipes adorned with colored feathers. As they walked, they raised the calumets above their heads as if offering them to the sun god.

A few feet from the Frenchmen, the old men stopped and looked fixedly at their visitors.

"Who are you?" the Frenchmen asked.

"Illinois," was the reply.

Jolliet and Marquette knew then that they were among friendly Indians.

In token of peace, the old men offered the calumets to the visitors. In token of peace, Jolliet and Marquette accepted the calumets, each putting the free end of a long stem to his mouth and smoking or making pretense of smoking the ceremonial pipe. The old men then invited the Frenchmen to visit their village.

At the door of the lodge to which Jolliet and Marquette were led stood an old man, naked and with his hands lifted toward the sun as if protecting his face from its rays.

"How beautiful the sun is, Frenchmen, when you come to visit us," he said to his guests in his native tongue. "All our village waits for you, and in peace you shall enter all our dwellings." Having welcomed the Frenchmen, the old man stood aside and ushered them into his lodge.

Inside the lodge, Jolliet and Marquette saw in the dusky light a crowd of natives who stared in heavy silence at the visitors. Now and then, the silence was broken by low voices speaking in the Indian tongue: "How good it is, my brothers, that you visit us."

When Jolliet and Marquette had taken their seats of honor among the elders of the village, a calumet was again offered to them. It was accepted by them as a sign of friendship. Then it was smoked by the elders to do honor to their visitors.

As the calumet was being passed from elder to elder, an invitation arrived from the great chief of all the Illinois to come to his village for a council. In the words of the Narrator:

"We went thither in a large Company, For all these people, who had never seen any Frenchmen among Them, could not cease looking at us. They Lay in The grass along the road; they preceded us and then retraced their steps to come and see us Again. All this was done noiselessly, and with marks of great respect for us."

When Jolliet and Marquette reached the village, they saw the great chief between two old men at the entrance of his lodge. All three stood erect and naked, the chief holding his calumet toward the sun.

With solemn dignity, the chief congratulated the strangers upon their arrival, offered them the calumet, and ushered them into his lodge, where the council was to be held.

Knowing the language of presents that was well understood by Indians of all nations, the explorers had brought with them a quantity of hatchets, knives, and other articles highly valued in the wilderness.

"Seeing all assembled and silent," the Narrator relates, "I spoke to them by four presents that I gave them. By the first, I told them that we were journeying peacefully to visit the nations dwelling on the

River as far as the Sea. By the second, I announced to them that God, who had Created them, had pity on Them, inasmuch as, after they had so long been ignorant of him, he wished to make himself Known to all the peoples; that I was Sent by him for that purpose; and that it was for Them to acknowledge and obey him. By the third, I said that the great Captain of the French informed them that he it was who restored peace everywhere; and that he subdued The Iroquois. Finally by the fourth, we begged them to give us all the Information that they had about the Sea and about the Nations through Which we must pass to arrive there."

When this speech was ended, the chief rose. With one hand resting on the head of a ten-year-old Indian boy, he replied in his native language with gravity and dignity:

"I thank you Black Gown, and you, Frenchman, for having taken so much trouble to come to visit us. Never has the earth been so beautiful, or the sun so bright, as today. Never has our river been so calm or so clear of rocks, which your canoes have removed in passing. Never has our tobacco tasted so good, or our corn appeared so fine, as we see them now. Here is my son, whom I give you to show you my heart. I beg you to have pity on me, and all my nation. It is you who know the Great Spirit who has made us all. It is you who speak to Him and who hear His word. Beg Him to give me life and health, and to come and dwell with us, in order to make us know Him."

At the end of his speech, the chief placed the Indian boy near the Frenchmen to signify that he was to be theirs as a slave. Then he presented a second gift, a calumet, considered more valuable than the boy. With the calumet, which was intended to assure his guests safe conduct on their voyage, the chief wished to express his esteem for the great captain of the French. With a third gift, he begged his guests not to go farther because of the terrible dangers to which they would expose themselves.

The council was followed by a feast. The first course was sagamité. The second was freshly cooked fish. The third was a large dog that had recently been killed. The fourth was the fat meat of the "wild ox" or buffalo. When the Indians learned that their guests did not eat dog meat, the third course was removed. Spoonfuls or morsels of the other food were picked up by a master of ceremonies and placed in the mouths of the guests, "As one would give food to a bird."

The next day, in taking leave of the chief and his people, Jolliet and Marquette promised to pass through the village again "within four moons." The chief conducted the Frenchmen to their birchbark canoes, which were greatly admired by the Illinois, most of whom had "never seen any like them." The water craft of the Illinois were heavy dugouts or pirogues, some of them more than fifty feet long, made from the trunks of trees. Nearly six hundred Indians were present at the leave-taking to give "every possible manifestation of joy" that the visit had brought them.

In saying adieu, Marquette promised the Illinois that he would come the next year to live among them and instruct them.

After resuming their journey downstream, the Frenchmen, with the small Indian slave, passed the mouths of several rivers that flowed into the Mississippi. In the Narrative, mention is made of the swift, muddy Pekitanoui (the Missouri) and the Waboukigou (the Ohio).

"After a month's Navigation," the Narrator relates, "while descending Missisipi from the 42nd to the 34th degree, and beyond, and after preaching the Gospel as well as I could to the Nations that I met, we start on the 17th of July from the village of the akansea, to retrace our steps. We therefore reascend the Missisipi which gives us much trouble in breasting its Currents. It is true that we leave it, at about the 38th degree, to enter another river which greatly shortens our road and takes us with little effort to the lake of the Ilinois."

The river that greatly shortened their way is known today as the

Illinois. It was not named in the Narrative of the voyage nor on Marquette's map. In 1679, Jolliet told Father Dablon that this river was named the St. Louis. On a map he made in that same year, he named it Rivière de la Divine. Even after "Rivière des Ilinois" became the name used on most maps, the river was sometimes referred to as the Divine.

By any name or no name, the river impressed both Jolliet and Marquette:

"We have seen nothing like this river that we enter, as regards its fertility of soil, its prairies and woods; its cattle, elk, deer, wildcats, bustards [geese], swans, ducks, parroquets, and even beaver. There are many small lakes and rivers. That on which we navigate is wide, deep, and still, for 65 leagues [about 180 miles]."

Jolliet told Father Dablon:

"The River which we have named the St. Louis and which rises near the lower end of the Lake of the Ilinois seemed to me to be the most beautiful and the most suitable for settlement. At the place where we entered the lake is a harbor, very convenient for receiving vessels and giving them shelter from the wind. This river is wide and deep, filled with catfish and sturgeons. Game is there in abundance, oxen, cows, stags, does, Turkeys, in much greater numbers than elsewhere. For a distance of 80 leagues, I was not a quarter of an hour without seeing some of them. There are prairies of six, ten, and 20 leagues in length and three wide, surrounded by forests of the same extent."

Nearly 250 miles up the river, between present-day Utica and Ottawa, the seven Frenchmen and the Indian boy came upon an Illinois village of seventy-four lodges. On Marquette's map the word "Kachkask" and the sign for two Indian wigwams mark the spot.

The Indians at the Kaskaskia village welcomed the strangers warmly and persuaded Marquette that he should return later to instruct them. A chief and some of his young men guided the visitors up the river and one of its tributaries to a portage, where the canoes were carried to the headwaters of a stream (probably the present Chicago River) that flowed eastward into Lake Michigan. Before winter settled down over the land, the seven Frenchmen and the ten-year-old Indian boy had reached the Jesuit mission at De Pere.

Thus was the Illinois River discovered to the world. Its discovery was an accident, a mere incident in the exploration of a larger river. It had an importance that neither Jolliet nor Marquette could have foreseen.

Jolliet, after losing his men and his papers in the St. Lawrence River near Montreal, completed his journey to Quebec to report the exploration. He wanted to return to the Illinois country, where "a settler would not have to spend ten years in cutting and burning trees" but could "put his plow into the ground the same day he arrived there." He believed that the way into the new country could be eased by building a canal at the site of the portage between the river flowing east and the river flowing west (present Chicago and Des Plaines rivers). He petitioned King Louis XIV in France to be allowed to start a settlement in the country he and Marquette had explored.

Possibly loss of his journal and other records in the rapid above Montreal weakened any claims he might have had to the new country. Possibly the officials of France and New France had begun to look with more favor upon another explorer.

For nearly a year, Jolliet waited for a reply to his petition. Then, in a letter dated April 28, 1677, a minister of the King answered: "His Majesty is unwilling to grant to sieur Jolliet the permission he has asked to go and settle in the country of the Islinois."

From De Pere, Marquette returned to the Illinois country in the autumn of 1674, about a year after he had left it. Illness and bad weather kept him on the Chicago River until the following spring. A few days before Easter, he arrived at Kaskaskia. His visit to his friends there is described by Father Dablon:

"On at last arriving at the village, he was received as an angel from Heaven. After he had assembled at various times the Chiefs of the nation, with all the old men, . . . he resolved to address all in public, in a general assembly which he called together in the open Air, the Cabins being too small to contain all the people. It was a beautiful prairie, close to a village, which was Selected for the great Council; this was adorned, after the fashion of the country, by Covering it with mats and bearskins. . . . The audience was Composed of 500 chiefs and elders, seated in a circle around the father, and of all the Young men, who remained standing. They numbered more than 1,500 men, without counting the women and children, who are always numerous; the village was Composed of 5 or 600 fires. The father addressed all of the people, and he gave them 10 messages by means of ten presents which he gave them."

On Easter Sunday, three days later, Marquette addressed the Illinois again and "took possession of that land in the name of Jesus Christ, and gave to that mission the name of the Immaculate Conception of the blessed virgin."

When Marquette told the Indians that, because of his illness, he must leave them, they pleaded with him to return. This he promised to do as soon as possible, or to send others in his place.

After telling the Illinois of the affection he felt for them, Marquette "set out with so many tokens of friendship on the part of Those good people that, as a mark of honor, they chose to escort him for more than 30 leagues on the Road, vying with each other in taking Charge of his slender baggage."

Despite the earnest entreaties of the Illinois, Marquette never returned to them. He died, May 18, 1675, on his way back to Michilimackinac. With the going of Marquette and his slender baggage, the valley of the Illinois settled back to the simple ways of the Indians.

But not for long.

5.

The Fort of the Broken Heart

The death of Father Marquette left the Jesuit mission on the Illinois River without a missionary. Father Claude Allouez, veteran of many years among the Indians of the Great Lakes, was appointed to carry on the work Father Marquette had begun.

In a canoe with two other Frenchmen, the priest left Green Bay late in October, 1676, and paddled along the west shore of Lake Michigan to make his first visit to the new mission. Winter weather stalled the party for many weeks.

Father Allouez arrived at the village of the Kaskaskias in late April, six months after setting out from Green Bay and two years, almost to the day, after Father Marquette had sorrowfully left his friends for the last time. He was welcomed not by one tribe of Indians but by eight. The village now consisted not of 74 lodges, the number Marquette had seen on his first visit, but of 351 ranged along the bank of the river. The Kaskaskias had invited to their village seven tribes that lived near the Mississippi.

After a short visit, Father Allouez returned to Green Bay, believing he had laid a solid foundation for the mission by baptizing thirty-five children and one sick adult.

While Father Allouez was finding quiet satisfaction in baptizing Indians, a younger and more ambitious Frenchman in charge of a frontier fort on the St. Lawrence River was planning an empire. The younger man was René Robert Cavelier, Sieur de La Salle. The visions of empire that seethed in his brain included all of the western country known to or suspected by the French—the land drained by the Mississippi and most of its tributaries, of which the Illinois River was one.

Born in Rouen, France, son of a wealthy merchant, Robert Cavelier early showed a fondness for mathematics and an interest in the Jesuit society. The month before his seventeenth birthday, he took the first vows of the society. In college, he studied philosophy and theology. For three years he taught in a school for boys. But the life of a scholar, teacher, and monk was too confining for his restless, ambitious spirit. At the age of twenty-three, he was released from his vows. A few months later he arrived in Canada, where an elder brother, Jean Cavelier, was a priest of St. Sulpice.

Montreal at that time was a frontier village, subject to attack by the savage Iroquois Indians, south across the St. Lawrence River. La Salle was given a grant of land (where Lachine now is) to be developed as a fur-trading center and an outpost against Indian raids.

While Jolliet and Marquette were exploring the Mississippi, La Salle was developing his own grant and directing the building of Fort Frontenac on Lake Ontario (where Kingston, Ontario, now is). Two years later, he returned to France, where King Louis XIV raised him to the rank of untitled noble, gave him valuable trading rights in New France, and placed him in command of Fort Frontenac.

La Salle loved solitude and he loved power. At Fort Frontenac, he had both in large measure. As an outpost, the fort was far removed from civilization and it controlled the lucrative fur trade of a vast territory. But La Salle loved glory, too.

"If he had preferred gain to glory," a friend said of him, "he had only to stay at his fort, where he was making more than twenty-five thousand livres a year."

Back to France La Salle sailed. There, in a letter dated May 12, 1678,

*René Robert Cavelier, Sieur de La Salle, explorer
and dreamer of empire in New France.*

the King gave him permission to explore all of the western part of New France. The permission to explore included the right to engage in the fur trade in most of the region.

Even three hundred years ago, exploration required large funds, and La Salle spent several weeks raising money from his relatives and friends in France. For the rest of his life, he would divide his time and energies four ways: finding new lands, finding new funds, fighting off creditors, and seeking faithful followers.

Once a Jesuit himself, La Salle now became an enemy of the Jesuits as the powerful religious order, jealous of his power, became his enemy. Many of his financial difficulties, and much of the disloyalty

37

of his followers, he laid to plots of the Jesuits to kill his dream of empire.

With his precious letter from the King, La Salle sailed for New France on the *Saint-Honoré*. On board were thirty men he had hired—sailors, pilots, carpenters, mechanics—and a considerable amount of equipment. On board, also, and ready to join in the great adventure, was Henri de Tonty, an Italian officer La Salle had met in France.

Tonty was a young man of unusual energy, courage, and ability, and the metal hand he wore to replace a hand he had lost in battle became more a mark of distinction than a handicap, even in the wilderness. In the years ahead, Tonty and an Indian hunter, a Mohegan, were to be among the few men who were constant in loyalty to La Salle, the cold, taciturn dreamer of empire, who drove himself without mercy and expected his men to follow.

Exploration of the western country, La Salle decided, would require a ship suited to the large lakes that formed a convenient but sometimes treacherous water highway to the region. The water route from Lake Ontario into Lake Erie was by way of a short river, the Niagara. Midway of the river, the water from Lake Erie tumbled, splashed, and roared over great falls that blocked the way between Fort Frontenac and the western country. La Salle planned to build a ship above the falls.

Never one to wait for fair weather, La Salle, with men and supplies, and with Tonty second in command, set out from Fort Frontenac in a small sailing ship on December 24, 1678.

Above the falls of the Niagara, La Salle set carpenters to work building his ship, to be named the *Griffon*. On an August day eight months after the keel was laid, the *Griffon,* with its five small cannon, was towed into Lake Erie. La Salle and his followers chanted *Te Deum* and fired the cannon. Then, with canvas swelling in the breeze and with La Salle, three Recollet friars, workmen, and crew aboard—

thirty-four men in all—the *Griffon* set sail for Michilimackinac.

Three days after entering Lake Huron, the *Griffon* ran into a storm so violent that, even with yardarms and topmasts lowered, it was driven helplessly before the wind. All on board—all but one— fell on his knees to pray. The pilot, instead of praying, shouted curses against La Salle for bringing him to drown ignominiously in a freshwater lake after many glorious years of sailing the salt seas.

The day after the storm subsided, the *Griffon* arrived at Michilimack- inac and anchored in calm water behind the point of St. Ignace, from which Jolliet and Marquette had set out six years before on their exploration of the Mississippi. Indians at the Ottawa village on the sandy shore gazed in wonder at the "floating fort." Cannon of the *Griffon* boomed, and the Indians yelped in surprise.

With pomp and ceremony, La Salle's party went ashore and marched to the bark chapel of the village. In a mantle of scarlet bordered with gold, La Salle knelt at the altar. Around him knelt Jesuit priests in their black robes, Recollet friars in gray, soldiers, sailors, work- men, weather-beaten voyageurs, painted Indians.

As La Salle left the chapel, Ottawa chiefs welcomed him with kind words; Hurons saluted him with a volley from their muskets. Out on the lake rode the *Griffon,* surrounded by a hundred birchbark canoes, like a yearling bass among minnows.

A few days later, the *Griffon* sailed westward. Near an island at the entrance of Green Bay (probably present-day Washington Island), the ship dropped anchor. Here La Salle found that several of his men who had been sent ahead the year before had collected a large store of furs. He decided to send the *Griffon,* loaded with furs, back to the Niagara River with orders to return and meet him at the southern end of Lake Michigan.

With fourteen men (including the three Recollet friars) La Salle set out in four canoes that rode deep in the water with their heavy loads—arms, ammunition, supplies, and a forge for use of the French; hatchets, knives, and other merchandise for trading with Indians.

Stormy weather buffeted the canoes on the voyage southward along the west shore of Lake Michigan. Around the southern end of the lake La Salle and his followers paddled until they reached the mouth of the River of the Miamis or the St. Joseph River (where Benton Harbor and St. Joseph, Michigan, are now). Here La Salle decided to wait for Tonty and several of his men who, before the *Griffon* left the Niagara River, had been sent on an errand to Sault Ste. Marie.

November and cold weather had arrived. La Salle's men grumbled at the delay. They wanted to leave the mouth of the St. Joseph and reach the great Indian town on the Illinois River before their provisions ran out. To quiet the grumbling, La Salle set his men to work constructing a building "forty feet long and eighty broad, made with great square pieces of timber laid one upon the other." This was the beginning of Fort Miami.

At last Tonty and his men arrived. But where was the *Griffon?* More than enough time had passed for the ship to return from a trip to the Niagara River.

Early in December, La Salle decided he could wait no longer for his ship. Leaving four men at the new fort, La Salle and his party, thirty-three men in eight canoes, paddled a few miles up the St. Joseph to a portage (site of South Bend, Indiana) that led across five miles of flat, swampy land to the headwaters of a river flowing west (the Teakiki, now the Kankakee).

With their food supply almost gone, La Salle and his followers paddled down the widening stream through a gray, wintry prairie dotted with leafless trees. At first, the only signs of wildlife were the bleached bones of buffalo and the trails made by the big animals along the stream. The men grumbled and would have deserted if they had dared to brave the winter without their leader. One of them raised his gun to shoot La Salle in the back but was stopped by a companion. Two lean deer and a few geese and swans brought in by the Mohegan hunter warded off starvation. A buffalo bull pulled from a slough in which he was mired provided several meals.

As La Salle's party continued down river in the brief, chill December days from the Kankakee into the Illinois, the flat prairies gave way to wooded hills with occasional rugged cliffs between. On the first day of the new year, 1680, nearly a month after leaving the fort at the mouth of the St. Joseph, the men passed on their left a towering cliff or massive rock, seemingly taller than others near it, that rose directly from the water. The bank opposite the massive rock spread out in broad meadows bordered on the north by a range of distant hills. Within sight of the rock, between the river and the hills clustered the lodges of an Indian town. Many lodges—460 of them! Made of a framework of poles overlaid with closely woven mats of rushes, each was shaped like the arched top of a covered wagon. Most were large enough for four or five fires. (A fire served one or two families.) This was the great town of the Illinois. Here would be food!

But where were the Indians? No sounds, no signs of life in the wintry scene. No smoke rose from the lodges.

Stepping ashore, the party found the fires dead and the ashes cold. The Indians were away on their winter hunt, La Salle guessed. He had hoped to buy corn from them for his hungry followers.

Searching the town, La Salle's men found the caches, or covered pits, in which the Indians had stored their supplies of corn for food and for planting the following spring. For strangers to touch the corn in their absence would be to the Indians a grave offense. But so desperate was the need that La Salle took thirty minots of the precious grain—enough to last thirty men through the winter—hoping he would be able to find the owners and pay them for it.

Toward evening three days later, while on a lake formed by the widening of the river, La Salle and his men saw smoke rising above the woods ahead of them. At nine o'clock the following morning, as they rounded a sharp turn in a narrow part of the river, they found themselves on the edge of an Indian camp, probably a winter hunting camp of the Illinois whose corn they had taken. Wooden canoes or pirogues lined the banks of the river, and smoke spiraled up from the eighty huts in two villages, one on each bank.

Quickly La Salle arranged his eight canoes abreast. Quietly putting down their paddles, the men took up their firearms. With La Salle only half a musket shot from the village on one bank of the river and Tonty an equal distance from the village on the opposite bank, the current carried the eight canoes silently into the midst of the camp.

Suddenly, above the gentle sounds of the river and the winter woods, boomed a voice from one of the canoes, demanding to know if the unsuspecting Indians wanted peace or war. In an instant, all was confusion in the two villages. Warriors snatched up their weapons and dashed for cover. Women and children poured out of the huts and fled toward the nearest woods.

La Salle jumped ashore. He was closely followed by his men, all so eager for battle that he had to restrain them to prevent a massacre of the fleeing Indians.

A few minutes later, two chiefs appeared on a hillside near the village. One of them carried a calumet as a sign they wanted peace. La Salle, holding up a calumet he had brought, showed that he, too, wanted peace. When the Indians saw La Salle's calumet their "joy was as great as their apprehension had been." Villagers from both sides of the river gathered and joined in dancing and other festivities that lasted all through the day.

In the evening, La Salle called together the elders of the two villages. Most of the young men were away on the winter hunt.

After making the elders gifts of tobacco and a few hatchets, La Salle told them he had summoned them to deal with a matter he wished to explain before speaking of any other.

He knew, he said, how precious their corn was to them. But, when he arrived at their village up the river, he was in such great need of supplies for his men that he had taken some of the corn, which was now in the canoes but not yet touched. If the Illinois could let him have the corn, he would give in exchange hatchets and other tools for which they had great need. However, if they could not furnish him with the corn he needed, he would go to their neighbors, the Osages, to buy food from them.

Jealous of letting La Salle go to another nation, the Illinois quickly accepted the hatchets and other tools. They even offered him more corn for more hatchets and begged him to live among them.

La Salle replied that he wanted to settle among the Illinois and would do so if they would agree to live at peace with the Iroquois. The Iroquois, he said, were subjects of the King of France and therefore his brothers. He could not make war against them. But he would defend the Illinois against Iroquois attacks if the Illinois would let him build a fort.

The elders agreed to his proposal, told him the mighty river he planned to explore was very beautiful, and that the sea was only twenty days distant by that river.

The following morning, La Salle noted, the elders were cold toward him and sullen. What had happened in the night?

As La Salle wondered about the cause of the change, he was approached by Omoahoha, a chief whose friendship he had won by a gift of two hatchets and three knives.

Late at night, said Omoahoha, the elders in secret council had listened to the words of Monso, a Mascouten chief, who had stealthily arrived in the Illinois camp. La Salle, claimed Monso, was a friend

43

of the Iroquois and planned to exterminate the Illinois. To convince the council of the truth of his words, Monso had brought gifts—kettles, hatchets, and knives. (La Salle suspected that the gifts had been supplied by his enemies the Jesuits.)

La Salle thanked Omoahoha for the information, gave him ten balls and ten shots of powder for his gun, and waited for an opportunity to refute Monso's accusations.

A few hours later, Nicanapé, one of the Illinois chiefs, gave a feast for La Salle and all of his men. Before the meal, the chief addressed the Frenchmen. He said that his reason for feasting them was not to satisfy their hunger but to cure their spirits of the sickness they had of wanting to descend a river that no one had ever descended before without dying. He said that the friendship he had for the Frenchmen obliged him to warn them against the dangers of the mighty river—the barbaric nations they would meet along the banks, the serpents and monsters in the water, the swift rapids, precipitous falls, and violent currents, and finally a whirlpool where the river lost itself and came out below the earth, no one knew where.

La Salle, watching his men closely, saw apprehension and fear grow in their faces as the chief proceeded. When Nicanapé had finished his speech, La Salle replied that the perils the chief described might be inventions of some evil spirit that had caused him to distrust the French.

"If the friendship you say you bear us is true, . . . do not disturb the joy that you showed at our arrival by stories that cause us to believe that joy was only on your lips," La Salle said.

After the feast, La Salle spoke again.

"I was not sleeping, my brother Nicanapé," he said, "when Monso gave you the false picture of the French—when at night and in secret he described us as spies of the Iroquois. The kettles and other gifts which he gave you to confirm these lies are still in this

44

hut where you buried them. Why did he flee immediately after his wicked act? If he is not a liar, let him speak in daylight as I do.

"Do you not see that I could have allowed your nephews to be killed in the confusion they were in at my arrival?" he asked. "In this hour in which I speak, while your young warriors are away hunting, could not my men slaughter all those of you who are old and for the most part defenseless?"

The speech so moved the Illinois that they promised to pursue Monso in the morning and bring him back to face La Salle.

Snow fell that night. It covered Monso's tracks. But it did not cool the plot of six of La Salle's men who had been terrified by Nicanapé's stories of monsters in the mighty river. When La Salle left his hut during the night, he saw no sentry on duty. Entering the hut of the men assigned to the guard, he found only one of his followers. The other six had fled in terror, preferring the hardships of the winter wilderness to the unknown dangers of the river.

Fearing that the Illinois might become hostile or that the Iroquois might invade the area, and wanting to keep his remaining followers away from the terror tales of Nicanapé, La Salle decided to leave the Indian camp and build a fort.

During a thaw in the middle of January, 1680, La Salle and his men paddled downstream a mile or more from the Indian camp and on a hill about two hundred yards from the river began building the first "civilized settlement" on the Illinois River.

Huts for the men were built of bullet-proof timber at two corners of a square. A hut for the three Recollet friars and a hut for the forge and the ammunition were built at the other two corners. On the four sides of the square, posts were placed upright in the ground to form a palisade twenty-five feet high. Tents for La Salle and Tonty were set up within the palisade.

The fort was called Crèvecoeur, so named, according to one of the

45

Fort Crèvecoeur, said to be the first "civilized settlement" on the Illinois River.

Recollet friars, "because the desertion of our men, with the difficulties we labored under, had almost broken our hearts."

While the fort was being built, a 42-foot keel was laid for the boat La Salle thought he needed for exploring the Mississippi. At the end of February, the fort was nearly completed and the hull of the boat was half finished.

By this time, La Salle was almost convinced that the *Griffon* was lost. The nearest rigging and other tackle needed for the boat being built was at Fort Frontenac, about a thousand crow-flight miles away. Because of the state of his financial affairs, La Salle decided that only he would be able to procure the supplies needed.

He waited until he had seen two of his most trusted Frenchmen and Father Louis Hennepin, one of the Recollet friars, start downstream to explore the lower Illinois River and the upper Mississippi. Then, with four Frenchman and the Mohegan hunter in two canoes, he started for distant Fort Frontenac.

Although the first day of March had arrived, winter still gripped river, woods, and prairies. About fifty miles above the deserted Illinois village, La Salle and his men found the river frozen. They hid their canoes on an island and continued their journey on foot. Between them and Fort Frontenac streched a vast country claimed by four or five Indian nations not altogether friendly. Their route was one often used by Iroquois war parties on their way west.

To one of his friends, La Salle later wrote that "the fatigue of enduring throughout the journey the discomforts of hunger, of sleeping on the ground in the open, quite often without eating, of being on sentry duty at night and walking by day, loaded with our baggage, such as blanket, clothing, kettle, ax, lead, powder, gun, and skins to make shoes; . . . sometimes pushing through thickets, sometimes climbing on rocks covered with ice and snow, sometimes walking entire days in swamps with water to the waist, or higher, in a season in which

47

the snow was not entirely melted; all that did not prevent me from determining to leave the fort to go on foot to Fort Frontenac to learn there myself news of my boat and to bring back the things we needed."

Sixty-five days after leaving Fort Crèvecoeur, La Salle arrived at Fort Frontenac. He had traveled almost constantly, had covered approximately a thousand miles, and had left his companions exhausted along the way. Of the six men who had set out from Fort Crèvecoeur, only he was able to complete "the most arduous journey ever made by Frenchmen in America."

Back in the Illinois country, Tonty remained at Fort Crèvecoeur with two Recollet friars and thirteen other Frenchmen, most of them in a mood for mutiny.

6.

Black Desolation

A few weeks after La Salle left Fort Crèvecoeur, two of his men arrived there from Fort Miami at the mouth of the St. Joseph River. They had been sent by La Salle, who had seen them on his way to Fort Frontenac.

They brought orders that Tonty should build a fort at the top of the Rock, the massive cliff that rose out of the Illinois near the great Indian village. Also, they brought news and rumors to feed the discontent of men who had not been paid for two years—men who were weary of wilderness hardships and on the verge of mutiny.

The *Griffon* was lost, the new arrivals reported. They had made a circuit of the lake without seeing or hearing of the ship. Fort Frontenac had been seized by La Salle's creditors. La Salle had been ruined financially and might never be able to pay his men.

Leaving most of the men at Fort Crèvecoeur to work on the boat, Tonty canoed up river with the two Recollet friars and three other Frenchmen to begin fortification of the Rock.

Only two of the men at Fort Crèvecoeur remained loyal to La Salle. The others grumbled, schemed, and plotted. Taking furs, provisions, ammunition, and other valuables with them, they set out for Fort Miami, Michilimackinac, and Fort Frontenac. Before leaving, they scrawled on the unfinished boat, *"Nous sommes touts sauvages"*— "We are all savages."

Henri de Tonty, faithful follower of La Salle. Tonty wore an iron hand to replace the one he had lost in battle.

Early in September, a Shawnee brave on his way home from a visit to the great Indian village near the Rock discovered a war party of Iroquois six hundred strong advancing into Illinois territory. In haste he returned to warn his friends.

Confusion and panic erupted in the Illinois village. Warriors snatched up their weapons. Women screamed and children cried. Excited Indians gathered about Tonty, accusing him of treachery.

La Salle had left the territory. Then other Frenchmen had left. Now, said the Illinois, La Salle and his Frenchmen were returning with the hated enemy, the Iroquois.

Terror seized the Illinois as they realized that fewer than five hundred of their warriors remained in the village. The others had gone to wage war on another enemy, the Sioux. Picking up such belongings as they could carry in haste, the Illinois loaded themselves into pirogues that lay along the bank and paddled down river several miles to an island almost surrounded by swampy land. Leaving the women and children there with sixty men to guard them, most of the warriors paddled back to the village.

In the light of fires blazing along the shore, they spent the night preparing for battle. They greased their bodies, painted their faces, stuck feathers in their hair, danced their war dances, sang their war songs, brandished their war clubs.

Scouts sent out at the first news of the Iroquois approach returned to say that a force of Miamis had joined the Iroquois. Having seen an Iroquois chief wearing a French hat and vest, they reported that La Salle was among the invaders.

The Illinois were now doubly convinced that Tonty had betrayed them. Wild with terror and rage, they surrounded him, threatening to tomahawk him and all the Frenchmen with him.

Handicapped by his imperfect knowledge of Indian language, Tonty tried to assure the Illinois that the report about La Salle was false. To prove it, he offered to join in the fight against the Iroquois.

Whooping their battle cries, the Illinois warriors dashed down to the river, pushed off in their pirogues, and paddled to the south bank. Tonty and his Frenchmen followed.

About a hundred of the Illinois were armed with guns, the others with bows and arrows. Running, leaping, and twisting to dodge enemy bullets and arrows, the Illinois advanced against the invading Iroquois.

The rapid clatter of guns from the Iroquois army told Tonty that the Illinois were at a disadvantage in both weapons and number of warriors and that the battle would probably go against them.

Putting down his own firearms and holding in his hand a belt of wampum as a sign he wanted peace, Tonty advanced toward the Iroquois through a rain of lead and arrows. Two Frenchmen and an Illinois joined him. When the firing continued, he sent back his companions and advanced alone.

Infuriated Iroquois swarmed about him. One of them jerked the wampum belt from his hand. A young brave plunged a knife into his chest. The blade glanced against a rib, inflicted a deep gash, but missed his heart. Suffering from the wound in his chest and from a blow he had received on his mouth, Tonty was hurried to the rear of the Iroquois army.

With the help of a chief who understood French, Tonty reminded the Iroquois that they were supposed to be at peace with the French— that the Illinois were under the protection of the King of France and the Governor of New France. He demanded to know why the Iroquois wished to break with the French rather than continue the peace.

He was interrupted by the arrival of a warrior who reported breathlessly that one wing of the Iroquois force was giving way, that Frenchmen had been seen among the Illinois, and that the Frenchmen had been shooting at the Iroquois.

This news infuriated the Iroquois further. They held a council. One chief argued for burning Tonty at the stake, one for setting him free. While the argument was going on, an Iroquois brave with a knife in his hand stood behind Tonty and now and then lifted his hair.

In this desperate situation, Tonty boasted to the Iroquois that the Illinois force numbered twelve hundred warriors and that sixty Frenchmen were at the Indian village ready to help them.

Although the Iroquois suspected that Tonty's boast was a lie, they could not be sure. They decided to try deception of their own. They sent Tonty back to the Illinois with a wampum belt to signify that both they and the Illinois were children of the Governor of New France and ought to make peace.

Faint from loss of blood but holding the wampum belt high, Tonty left the Iroquois army and staggered across the space between the warring forces. The firing tapered off and ceased. Back among the Illinois, Tonty delivered the wampum belt to the chiefs. But he warned against trusting the ones who sent it.

An uneasy truce began.

The Illinois warriors crossed the river to their village. The Iroquois, a few at a time, followed, asking for food. Suspecting treachery, the Illinois warriors set fire to their village and paddled down river to the island where they had left their women and children.

The Iroquois took over what remained of the village and built a rude fort some distance from Tonty's cabin. They insisted that Tonty go to the Illinois with an offer of a treaty of peace.

Taking with him an Iroquois warrior as a hostage, Tonty paddled down river to the island where the Illinois had taken refuge. Leaving the Iroquois hostage on the island, Tonty returned to the Iroquois camp with a hostage from the Illinois. Unfortunately, the unwary Illinois hostage told the Iroquois how few of his nation's warriors were in the vicinity and said that, if the Iroquois really wanted peace, the Illinois were ready to give them beaver skins and slaves.

In anger, the Iroquois called Tonty to them. He was a liar, they said, to have told them the Illinois had twelve hundred warriors. And where were the sixty Frenchmen Tonty had told them were in the village?

"I had much difficulty in getting out of the scrape," Tonty wrote later. He must have been successful for, the following day, the chiefs of the two forces met a short distance from the Iroquois fort to conclude a treaty of peace. The Iroquois gave presents and a promise that hereafter the two nations should live as brothers. The presents convinced the Illinois of the sincerity of the Iroquois. But Tonty, who knew that the Iroquois were secretly building canoes of elm bark, warned the Illinois that "they had everything to fear" and that they should leave their island and join some distant friendly nation.

The eighth day after the battle, the Iroquois called Tonty and one of the Recollet friars to a council. When the council had assembled, the Iroquois placed six packets of beaver skins before their guests. The first two packets, they said, were to inform Governor Frontenac that they would not eat his children and that he should not be angry at what they had done. The third packet represented a plaster for Tonty's wound, the fourth some oil to rub on the tired bodies of Tonty and the friar, who had traveled far. The fifth packet signified that the sun was bright, and the sixth that Tonty and his Frenchmen should take advantage of it and leave the next day for the French settlements in Canada. In reply, Tonty asked the Iroquois when they themselves would leave the territory. The Iroquois murmured. Some of them said they would eat Illinois flesh before they left.

At this, Tonty kicked away the beaver skins. He would have none of them, he said, if the Iroquois planned to eat the children of the Governor.

Angered at the rejection of their gifts, the Iroquois chiefs rose and drove Tonty and the friar from the council.

Tonty and his French companions spent the night in their cabin, constantly on guard and wondering if, in the morning, the sun would be bright for them. At daybreak, they left the village, paddling up river in a leaky canoe, not knowing what might be the fate of their friends the Illinois.

The Iroquois now turned from the living and made war on the dead.

Some of the Illinois dead had been buried in a cemetery near the village. Some had been laid to rest on scaffolds above ground, out of the reach of dogs and wolves. In blind fury, the Iroquois tore down the scaffolds, dug into graves, chopped up the corpses, threw pieces to the dogs, scattered the bones. The ends of fire-blackened poles and stakes that protruded from the ground as remnants of lodges they decorated with skulls of the dead.

They broke open the caches where the corn was stored and scattered the grain. They went to unharvested cornfields, trampled the stalks, threw some of the ears in heaps, and set them afire.

Having wreaked their fury on the dead, the Iroquois moved down river to pursue the living. Pretending friendship, they camped on the south bank opposite the island where the Illinois had taken refuge.

Unsure of the sincerity of the Iroquois, the Illinois moved down river to another campsite on the north bank. The Iroquois moved and camped on the south bank opposite the Illinois. Six times above Fort Crèvecoeur and four times below, the Illinois moved and the Iroquois followed. The last move brought the Illinois close to the Mississippi River.

In the Illinois camp, the food supply was running low. The tribes making up the Illinois band decided to separate. If they were in smaller bands, they could more easily obtain their food by hunting.

The Kaskaskias and the Cahokias moved up the Mississippi. The Peorias crossed to the west side of the river. Some of the tribes moved down the river. The Tamaroas and two smaller tribes, trustful of the Iroquois, remained near the mouth of the Illinois. They planned to do their hunting there.

With sudden fury, the Iroquois attacked. The Illinois warriors made a feeble resistance and then, seeing themselves greatly outnumbered, fled in terror, leaving their women and children to the fury of the Iroquois.

On November 4, forty-five days after Tonty and his companions had been driven by the Iroquois from the Illinois village near the Rock, La Salle arrived at the mouth of the St. Joseph River. With him, in heavily laden canoes collected at Fort Frontenac, he had twenty-five men and everything he believed he needed for his boat and the exploration of the Mississippi.

La Salle had heard no recent news of Tonty. Rumors that the Iroquois were on the warpath made him uneasy. Leaving most of his men at the mouth of the St. Joseph in charge of François Daupin, Sieur de La Forest, he pushed on toward the Illinois River with six Frenchmen and the Mohegan hunter. He hoped to find Tonty at either the Rock or Fort Crèvecoeur.

Up the St. Joseph he and his men paddled, portaged to the Kankakee, and paddled down the gently flowing stream into the Illinois. As they neared the Rock, they saw in the wintry solitude no palisades, no signs of life. In the meadows across the river where nine months before they had left the Illinois village, they saw only black desolation.

As they pushed their canoes to the bank and landed, crows and buzzards rose flapping into the air; wolves left the human bodies they were feeding on and galloped away. Eyeless skulls stared at them from the ends of charred stakes, stakes that once had formed the framework of lodges.

Where were Tonty and his men? La Salle searched the fire-blackened village and the rude fort the Iroquois had built. He found fragments of French clothing, but among the skulls none with the hair of Europeans.

Though the frigid December night, which vibrated with the howling of wolves, La Salle lay awake by the bivouac fire, thinking, thinking, wondering what he should do. At length he decided to leave three of his men with most of the baggage and one canoe in a secluded spot near the ruined village and push on down the river. Perhaps the Illinois had taken Tonty with them when they left.

With three Frenchmen and the Indian, La Salle set out the next morning in the second canoe. Each man was armed with two muskets, a pistol, and a sword. In the canoe were hatchets and other goods for trading with Indians.

A few miles below the ruined village, La Salle and his party saw the island, now deserted, where the Illinois had taken refuge from the Iroquois. On the south bank opposite, they saw the abandoned camp of the Iroquois. They went ashore and counted the huts—113 of them. They discovered, carved on the trees that covered the hills behind the camp, the totems or insignia of the Iroquois chiefs and marks to show the number of warriors led by each. But they found no marks to indicate the fate of Tonty and his men.

Farther down the river, they passed the six Illinois campsites above Fort Crèvecoeur and the four below, each with an Iroquois campsite facing it on the opposite bank. At the abandoned fort, they found the boat on the stocks, with the nails gone and the sign left by the deserters: *"Nous sommes touts sauvages."*

When they arrived at the fourth campsite below Fort Crèvecoeur, they saw that ashes from the fires had been wet by neither rain nor snow and they knew that the Illinois had not been gone long from the place. In the hope that he would soon find Tonty with the Illinois, La Salle urged on his men, keeping them going through the night.

At noon of the following day, December 5, 1680, as they neared the Mississippi, they saw in the wintry meadow on their right the bodies of women and children who had been killed by the Iroquois. A search of the meadow revealed the lifeless bodies of three Iroquois and only a few Illinois warriors. La Salle knew then what had happened.

No Frenchmen nor signs of Frenchmen were found among the dead. Perhaps Tonty and his men still lived. La Salle pushed on with his men to the mouth of the Illinois, to the place where the waters of the

Illinois become the waters of the Mississippi. There he stopped.

His men urged him to go on, offering to risk their lives in the exploration he had set his heart upon. But La Salle declined their courageous offer. He preferred to wait until spring. Then he would have the help of the men left at Fort Miami. Besides, he did not want to abandon the three men he had left near the ruined village of the Illinois.

On December 7, when ice began to form on the Mississippi River, La Salle and his men started the return journey up the Illinois River. Before they set out, a picture of a canoe and a calumet was drawn on a piece of board brought from Fort Crèvecoeur. A small tree growing from a rock in a conspicuous place at the mouth of the Illinois was stripped of its branches, and the board was nailed to the trunk. To the board was attached a letter, written by La Salle, to inform Tonty (if he should ever read the letter) where he could find hidden several hatchets, knives, and other articles that might prove useful to him among the Indians. If the letter was seen by a passing Indian, La Salle believed, it would eventually reach Tonty.

A month later, at a fork in the river several miles above the ruined village of the Illinois, La Salle and his party turned the prows of their canoes into the Des Plaines, rather than the Kankakee. A few miles up the Des Plaines, they saw on the bank a rude cabin of bark. Near the cabin they discovered a piece of wood that had been cut with a saw. In the Illinois country in 1681, a piece of sawed lumber was a rare object, and to La Salle the small piece beside the bark cabin meant that Tonty had escaped from the Iroquois and had gone up the Illinois instead of down.

Impatient to know if Tonty was still alive, La Salle left his canoes and two of his men in the January cold beside the Des Plaines River and set out with the others across country toward the fort on the St. Joseph.

"It had snowed extraordinarily all day, and it kept on snowing for nineteen days in a row," La Salle wrote afterward to a friend. "The cold was extraordinarily rigorous. I have never seen in Canada such a harsh winter. We had to cross forty leagues of open country, where we could scarcely find, in the evening, wood to keep us warm and never wood from which we could take bark to build a shelter. We had to pass the nights exposed to a furious wind that swept across the plains. I can assure you that I never suffered so much from the cold. Nor have I had more trouble in going forward, because we could not use snowshoes; the snow was soft and as if suspended over the vegetation. It was sometimes up to my waist, although I am rather tall. Marching in front, as I have always done to encourage my men, while breaking a path I often had trouble striding over the snow, and I sometimes had to push through it with my body."

Tony was not at the fort on the St. Joseph, and no one there had news of him.

7.

Death of a Dream

At the mouth of the St. Joseph River, where a new and larger Fort Miami was beginning to take shape, La Salle found Indians from as far away as the Atlantic Coast gathered to seek protection from the Iroquois. In attacking the Illinois and driving them from their home territory, the Iroquois had spread new fear among the many tribes that in the past had been victims of their savagery.

Taking advantage of this fear, La Salle began building a defensive league or confederation that he hoped would insure the peace necessary for a profitable fur trade in the Illinois country. Abenakis and Mohegans from New England and Shawnees from the Ohio River valley already looked to La Salle for leadership and protection.

In March, after hearing from roving Indians that some of the Illinois had returned to their homeland, La Salle set out with La Forest and several other men to find his old allies.

Snow lay over the prairies and swamps, and a brilliant sun on the white expanse was so dazzling that La Salle and a few of his men became snow-blind. While La Forest with most of the men continued the journey, those suffering from snow-blindness camped at the edge of a forest with a man named Hunaut to care for them.

Sent in search of pine needles for making a decoction thought to be useful in treating snow-blindness, Hunaut returned with news as joyous as it was unexpected. He had not gone far when he discovered tracks that led to a camp of traveling Outagami or Fox Indians from the

Green Bay area. Did the Outagamis, by chance, have word of Henri de Tonty, dead or alive?

Tonty? Tonty was alive, the Outagamis reported. He was spending the winter with Potawatomis near Green Bay.

Hunaut hurried back to La Salle. Whether he carried pine needles as well as good news is not known.

Quietly rejoicing in Tonty's safety, La Salle continued his journey and soon met a band of Illinois Indians. He gave them presents and urged them to make peace with the Miamis. Pleased with the presents, the Illinois promised to carry La Salle's message to other members of their nation.

La Salle then returned to Fort Miami. From the fort, he and a few followers set out for an Indian village on the Kankakee to try to win over the Miamis, who sometimes fought with the Iroquois and sometimes against them. At the village, in addition to Miamis, were Indians from Rhode Island, New York, Virginia, and other eastern areas.

La Salle called a council of the eastern visitors. He promised them a new home in the West under the protection of the Great King of France—a new home with rich lands, good hunting, and French traders to supply them with goods such as they had once had from the English. He assured them of prosperity and safety if they would help him make peace between the Miamis and the Illinois. Members of the council listened thoughtfully and promised aid.

The following morning, La Salle attended a council of the Miamis. When the chiefs and elders had assembled, he rose to his feet and in the manner of Indian orators addressed the council. He began his speech with a gift of tobacco that, he said, was to clear the brains of his listeners. Then he presented the chiefs and elders with gifts for their dead relatives: cloth to cover them, coats to dress them in, hatchets for building a grand scaffold in their honor, and beads and other trinkets for decorating them at a grand funeral banquet. Both the

Miamis and La Salle understood that these articles given to compliment the dead were for the use of the living.

La Salle then told the council that the Miamis should live at peace with their neighbors, especially the Illinois.

"Let us all obey the Great King," he said, "and live together in peace, under his protection. Be of my mind, and use these guns that I have given you not to make war, but only to hunt and to defend yourselves."

To confirm his words, La Salle presented the council with two belts of wampum.

The Miami chiefs and elders met again the following day.

"The Illinois is our brother because he is the son of our Father, the Great King," they told La Salle. "We make you the master of our beaver and our lands, of our minds and our bodies."

La Salle had taken the first steps in bringing peace to the western empire. But he could not forget that the Mississippi was still unexplored. Late in May, 1681, he began the long canoe voyage to Fort Frontenac and Montreal to make, for the third time, preparations for exploration of the Mississippi. At Michilimackinac, he was finally joined by Tonty. At Fort Frontenac and Montreal, he was met by his creditors. Through the assistance of Governor Frontenac and the support of a wealthy relative, he was able to quiet his creditors and even to obtain more funds for his enterprise.

With some of his men in heavily laden canoes, La Salle was back at Fort Miami in December, 1681. Tonty with the other men and canoes had reached the fort ahead of him and was ready for exploration of the Mississippi.

In the exploring party were twenty-three Frenchmen and eighteen Mohegan and Abenaki warriors. The Indians, "all inured to war," insisted on taking along ten of their squaws to cook for them. The squaws had three children.

Tonty, with all of the canoes (six in number) and most of the men, set out six days before Christmas along the south shore of Lake Michigan.

"We went in canoes to the River Chicaou where there is a portage which joins that of the Islinois," Tonty wrote in reporting on the expedition.

Three days after Christmas, La Salle and the rest of the men left Fort Miami on foot and followed the sandy south shore of the lake. On January 6, they joined the larger group camped on the Des Plaines River. The streams were frozen, and Tonty already had the canoes on sledges.

In a long procession, the exploring party dragged the sledges, loaded with canoes, baggage, and provisions, over the frozen surface of the river, past the great Illinois village, standing deserted in the winter landscape, and on to open water and the winter camp of a band of Illinois Indians at Pimitoui (Peoria Lake).

Leaving Pimitoui toward the end of January, 1682, La Salle and his party arrived at the mouth of the Illinois on February 6. Floating ice on the Mississippi kept them there until the thirteenth, when the six canoes glided out into the waters of the great river and headed downstream.

Late in June, 1682, La Salle and his party were again at the mouth of the Illinois. In five and a half months they had explored the Mississippi to the Gulf of Mexico and claimed for the King of France the entire valley from the source of the river in the far north to the mouth of the river at the Gulf and from the green wooded ridges of the Alleghenies on the east to the bleak bare peaks of the Rockies on the west, a sizable chunk of land even for a king.

Exploration of the Mississippi had only interrupted progress of the Indian defensive league La Salle hoped would bring peace and prosperity to his empire. In less than a year after taking possession of the

Mississippi River valley, La Salle could look down from the palisades of a newly completed Fort St. Louis atop the Rock (later to be known as Starved Rock), and see hundreds of Indian lodges of bark or rushes clustered in the meadows that bordered the river. Four thousand warriors—twenty thousand men, women, and children—were the number of Indian allies La Salle reported to an official of the King. Brought together by fear of a common enemy and the hope of trading with the French, the Illinois, Miamis, Shawnees, Mohegans, Abenakis, and others represented a triumph for La Salle's hard work and skillful diplomacy among the Indians.

Although usually successful in his dealings with Indians, La Salle often failed in relationships with his countrymen. Governor Frontenac had been his friend and had protected him from powerful men in Quebec and Montreal who were jealous of his rich monopolies in the fur trade. But, in 1682, Frontenac was replaced as governor by an old naval officer, Antoine Le Febvre de la Barre. Soon after, La Salle found that *coureurs de bois* he had sent to Montreal for supplies were being held there by his enemies. Not only was La Barre cutting off La Salle from supplies needed for trading with the Indians at Fort St. Louis, he was telling the Iroquois they had permission to kill La Salle and plunder his holdings.

La Salle saw only one way to save his empire from destruction. Leaving Tonty in charge of Fort St. Louis, he set out in August, 1683, for Quebec. He was bound for France to see the King.

A month later, an officer of the King's dragoons arrived in the Illinois country with orders from La Barre that Tonty was to give up the command at Fort St. Louis and with news that La Barre's agents had seized Fort Frontenac, sold La Salle's goods for their own profit, and turned cattle in to graze on the growing crops.

The following spring, Tonty made the long trip to Quebec, where he met La Forest, who had gone with La Salle to France and had

The Rock, site of first fort St. Louis, and now known as Starved Rock.

returned with good news. La Salle had seen the King. Fort Frontenac and his western empire had been restored to him, and he was sailing for the Gulf of Mexico to find the mouth of the Mississippi and establish a colony there. He had asked the King for two ships. The King had given him four.

When Tonty returned to Fort St. Louis as its commander in the summer of 1685, he found that La Salle's Indian league had begun to fall apart. The Miamis and the Illinois had fought, and the Miamis had won a decisive victory.

Without La Salle, Tonty was restless. Less than six months after his return to Fort St. Louis, he was at Michilimackinac seeking news of his commander. He learned that La Salle had arrived in the Gulf of Mexico. In the middle of February, 1686, he left Fort St. Louis with a party of Frenchmen and Indians on a voyage down the Mississippi to find his leader.

At the Gulf of Mexico, the men he sent out in two canoes, one east and the other west, to search for La Salle brought back oysters and a porpoise, but no news of La Salle, his four ships, or his colony. By late June Tonty returned to the Illinois country.

September, 1687, had come to the Illinois River. Reds and yellows had begun to creep into the greens along the water and on the distant hills. At the top of the Rock that rose like a sheer wall from the river near the great Illinois village, Fort St. Louis dozed in the late summer sun.

In command of the fort was the Sieur de Bellefontaine, for Tonty was many miles to the east, fighting the Iroquois, and La Salle was—no one knew where. More than a year had passed since Tonty had made his fruitless search at the Gulf of Mexico. Even in the absence of La Salle and Tonty, the garrison felt safe, for the naturally strong position had been strengthened by palisades and by houses of heavy timber built along the edge of the rock. To the small force of French

66

soldiers and *coureurs de bois* had been added a number of friendly Indians, and their lodges squatted on top of the Rock not far from the spacious drill ground, the chapel, and the warehouse.

About two in the afternoon of the fourteenth, the Sabbath quiet of the fort was interrupted by the arrival of two Indian runners. A short distance downstream they had seen a large wooden canoe with five Frenchmen—two of them priests—and three Indian guides. La Salle was coming—or some of his men!

Down to the river hurried a Frenchman and several Indians to salute the travelers with a volley from their muskets.

The canoe touched the south bank, and the travelers stepped ashore: Father Jean Cavelier (La Salle's brother), Father Anastasius Douay (a Recollet friar), Henri Joutel (one of La Salle's officers), young Cavelier (seventeen-year-old nephew of La Salle), one of La Salle's men named Teissier, and three Indian guides from the Arkansas River. They were met by the Sieur Boisrondet, clerk to La Salle, and two other Frenchmen.

Where was La Salle? Boisrondet asked the question almost at once.

La Salle? Oh, he had brought them part way and had left them, explained Father Cavelier and Henri Joutel. He was in good health when last they saw him. Father Douay, the man named Teissier, and young Cavelier kept silent.

In the fort, the travelers found Frenchmen of the garrison drawn up in formation to welcome them with several volleys from their muskets. They were then conducted to the chapel, where they gave thanks to God for having preserved them from death, and finally to their lodgings. The Indians living at the fort stopped by again and again, firing their muskets "to express their joy" at arrival of the travelers and news of La Salle.

The travelers were still at the fort when Tonty returned from the Iroquois war.

What was the news of La Salle? To Tonty as to Boisrondet, Father Cavelier and Joutel replied that La Salle was in good health when last they saw him. Again Father Douay, young Cavelier, and Teissier kept silent. The following spring, Father Cavelier and his party resumed their journey up the Illinois on their way to France.

On a September day two years after Jean Cavelier had given assurance at Fort St. Louis of his brother's good health, a French carpenter named Couture arrived at the fort from a settlement in the Arkansas country. Father Cavelier and his party, stopping at the settlement on their way to the Illinois River, had told Couture an important fact they had concealed from Tonty. La Salle was dead.

Disaster had fallen on La Salle's attempts to find the mouth of the Mississippi and establish a colony there. Of his four ships that sailed from France on July 24, 1684, one had been captured by Spaniards, two had gone aground in the Gulf of Mexico, and the fourth had returned to France. Most of his provisions and equipment had been lost. Several of the 280 men and women who left France with La Salle had been killed by Indians. Some had deserted.

The attempt to find the mouth of the Mississippi from the Gulf having failed, La Salle had begun a settlement in Texas, many miles west of the mouth. He had then decided to return to the Illinois country and eventually to France to obtain help for his unfortunate colony.

With more than a dozen men and five horses, he had begun the overland journey northward on January 12, 1687. In the party were Father Cavelier, Father Douay, Joutel, and young Cavelier. Also in the party were several men who harbored grudges against their leader.

On the way out of the Texas country, some of the malcontents had turned conspirators and secretly murdered three of the faithful. Then, early on the morning of March 20, as La Salle came searching for his missing men, one of the conspirators had shot their leader in the head.

Father Douay had seen La Salle fall. Father Cavelier and Joutel had not. La Salle had been in good health when last they saw him.

"Such was the end of one of the greatest men of this age, a man of an admirable spirit, and capable of undertaking all sorts of explorations," wrote Tonty, La Salle's most famous follower.

"Such was the unfortunate end of M. de La Salle's life, at a time when he might entertain the greatest hopes, as the reward of his labors," wrote Joutel, aware of both the virtues and the vices of his leader. "He had a capacity and talent to make his enterprise successful; his constancy and courage, and his extraordinary knowledge in arts and sciences, which rendered him fit for anything, together with an indefatigable body, which made him surmount all difficulties, would have procured a glorious issue to his undertakings, had not all those excellent qualities been counterbalanced by too haughty a behavior, which sometimes made him insupportable, and by a rigidness towards those that were under his command, which at last drew on him implacable hatred and was the occasion of his death."

With La Salle died his bright dream of empire.

8.

Under Three Flags

In the fifth September after the death of La Salle, young Pierre Liette, in command of Fort St. Louis on the Rock, received a letter from his relative Henri de Tonty at Michilimackinac.

Monsieur de La Forest, Tonty wrote, had been successful in an appeal he had made to King Louis XIV. He had seen the King and had secured for himself and Tonty the trading rights that had belonged to La Salle. With soldiers and workmen, La Forest was returning to the Illinois country. In exchange for the trading rights, he had promised that he and Tonty would defend the region from all enemies of the King.

The Indians living near the Rock, Tonty reminded Liette, were growing dissatisfied with their village. They had to travel too far for their firewood and, if they were attacked and besieged, they would have difficulty in supplying themselves with water. Tonty instructed Liette to call together the chiefs and have them select a site for a new village.

The chiefs, meeting in council, chose a spot on the west shore of Lake Pimitoui, about a mile and a half from its lower end.

A few weeks later, in November of 1691, Tonty arrived at Fort St. Louis on the Rock, canoed about seventy miles downriver to the site of the new village, and began building a fort. The new fort was to be large enough to give both the French and their Indian allies protection from the Iroquois and other hostile tribes. Named Fort St. Louis, but

View from the top of the Rock. The population of the Indian village across the river varied from year to year.

often called Fort Pimitoui, the structure was completed the following spring, after the arrival of La Forest.

Inside the palisade of eighteen hundred pickets stood two large log houses, one for lodgings and one for a warehouse, and two other houses built of upright logs to shelter the soldiers.

For its first few years, the new Fort St. Louis knew prosperity and relative peace. Tonty and La Forest carried on a fur trade with little interference from French authorities and unfriendly Indians. To discourage the English and the Iroquois, who were threatening to capture the fur trade of the nearby Wabash River valley, Tonty regularly sent war parties east from the Illinois country. To prove to French authorities that he was active in defending the western domain from enemies of the King, he signed on April 11, 1694, a statement giving the numbers of Iroquois that the Illinois estimated they had killed or captured in the previous seven years: 334 men and boys and 111 women and girls.

Around the new Fort St. Louis gathered French traders, as well as friendly Indians, to form what has been called the first permanent settlement in the Illinois country.

In 1696, four years after the new fort was completed, King Louis XIV in faraway France issued an order prohibiting French traders from going into the wilderness to collect furs. The order was prompted partly by conscience and partly by finances. The King had heard from forest missionaries of the great evils done to the Indians by brandy carried into the wilderness by fur traders. He had been told by his financial advisers of the high cost of the almost constant Indian wars caused by the struggle for good hunting and trapping territory.

From this time on, the Indians would have to bring their furs to Canadian villages. Fur traders and brandy would be kept out of the wilderness, where they did their greatest damage,

The King's order could not undo the harm the fur trade had already done. For many centuries before they first saw white men, the Indians had been village dwellers who lived by cultivating the soil and killing only as many wild animals as they needed for their own food and clothing. The fur trade had made them wandering hunters encouraged to kill animals for their fur alone. They had been independent, self-sustaining people who made their own weapons, tools, and clothing. The fur trade had made them subservient vassals, dependent on white men for their living and willing to trade their own and their neighbors' hunting grounds for brandy or whiskey and a few guns, knives, hatchets, kettles or blankets.

Tonty and La Forest were exempted from part of the King's order.

But they were instructed to do no more trading in beaver skins and were to be allowed to bring into the Illinois country only a limited amount of merchandise—as much each year as they could carry in two canoes navigated by not more than twelve men.

When Father Jean François Buisson de St. Cosme and fellow missionaries stopped at the new Fort St. Louis in 1698, they found that the settlement growing up about the fort had taken on several marks of French civilization. Many Indian children had been baptized, and a number of adults had renounced their superstitions and were living "as thoroughly good Christians." Some of the Indian women who were married to Frenchmen impressed St. Cosme by their modesty and by their faithfulness in going several times a day to prayer in the chapel.

At another village, they found a French soldier named La Viollette married to an Indian girl. The couple had a child, who was soon baptized by one of St. Cosme's fellow priests. Chief of the village was an Indian squaw.

"This woman," St. Cosme reported, "enjoys great repute in her nation, owing to her wit and her great liberality and because, as she has many sons and sons-in-law who are good hunters, she often gives feasts, which is the way to acquire the esteem of the savages and of all their nations in a short time."

New enemies were threatening the territory of the Illinois Indians when Father Pierre François Xavier de Charlevoix and his party canoed down the Illinois River in 1721. Three years before, the Outagami Indians from the north had invaded the valley, and their marauding bands were still there.

At the Fort St. Louis on Lake Pimitoui, Charlevoix and his companions were told that on their way from the old fort they had passed close to an ambuscade of thirty Outagami warriors, that an equal

Indian chief with pipe or calumet.
(From an original drawing
by an artist of New France.)

French trader bound for the
wilderness and the fur trade.

number of the enemy hovered about the village of Pimitoui, and that eighty warriors, in two bands, lurked downriver.

Surrounded by four bands of Outagami warriors, Charlevoix looked out from the fort and saw the Illinois River valley in October as a place of quiet beauty and prodigal abundance.

"Nothing can be more delightful than its situation," he wrote of the fort to a friend. "Opposite to it is the prospect of a most beautiful forest . . . adorned with all the variety of colors, and behind it is a plain of an immense extent, skirted with woods. The lake and the river swarm with fish, and the banks of both with game."

With fourteen well-armed men, some of them recruited from the fort, Charlevoix passed safely down the Illinois River and into the Mississippi. But, for seven or eight days afterwards, he was "not able to sleep with tranquility."

In 1730, two years before George Washington was born, the Outagamis in the Illinois country were almost exterminated by an army of fourteen hundred consisting of a few Frenchmen and their Indian allies: Illinois, Potawatomis, Miamis, and Sauks.

By the time Washington was a twenty-two-year-old lieutenant-colonel in the British colonial army, the French were pushing east and the British were pushing west in the Ohio River valley. They had an important meeting in 1754 when young Washington with a force of colonials was sent by Governor Robert Dinwiddie of Virginia to attack a small force of French and Indians at Fort Duquesne (later Fort Pitt, where Pittsburgh, Pennsylvania, now is).

The French and Indian War that followed was fought many miles east of the Illinois River, but some of the Indians of the valley traveled east to fight with the French against the British.

By the time the war was ended with the Treaty of Paris, signed in February, 1763, the Illinois River had ceased to be a very important part of the water highway between Canada and the West. Most of the traffic had shifted to the Wabash, the Ohio, and the Mississippi. Fort St. Louis was no longer the most important frontier post in the Illinois country. It had been replaced by Fort de Chartres on the Mississippi. The once numerous and powerful Illinois Indians, victims of the fur trade, alcohol, and disease introduced by white men, had dwindled in numbers and prowess. Of the survivors, only a few lived on the beautiful river that Jolliet had named the Divine. Most of them had moved to villages along the Mississippi. Sometimes, small bands of them returned to winter along the Illinois, or a few of their young men made hurried trips to steal horses from their old friends the French on Lake Pimitoui, which was gradually becoming known as Peoria Lake.

In the Treaty of Paris, the French ceded to the British the Illinois country and all their other possessions in North America except New Orleans. But before the British could take over the forts of the Illinois country, much of the vast territory wrested from the French had been lost to the Indians in an uprising led by one of the greatest of their chiefs, the Ottawa Pontiac.

Even before the Treaty of Paris was signed, Pontiac had begun his efforts to unite the Indian tribes against the British with a message from the Great Spirit.

"I am the Master of Life," began the message. "It is I who have made all men; consequently I ought to watch over their preservation. That is why I inform you that if you suffer the English among you, you are dead men. Sickness, smallpox, and their poison will destroy you entirely. It is necessary to pray to me and to do nothing contrary to my wishes. I will sustain you; but you must abandon your altar mats and your manitoes. Plurality of wives is contrary to my law."

The message reached Indians as far west as the Mississippi River and in May, 1763, the uprising began. Before the end of June, British forts in Michigan, Ohio, and Indiana fell before Pontiac's warriors.

Only Detroit, Fort Niagara, and Fort Pitt held out. Two years passed before the British were able to put down the uprising.

To Colonel George Croghan, Deputy Agent for Indian Affairs at Detroit, was given the task of arranging a peace treaty with Pontiac. Hearing that Pontiac was in the Illinois country, Colonel Croghan left Fort Pitt and started west to find the defeated chief. On the way, he met Pontiac and other chiefs traveling east. In a council held at Ouiatenon (near present Lafayette, Indiana) on the Wabash River, he "settled all matters with the Ilinois Indians."

To settle matters with other Indian tribes, Croghan and his assistants, supplied with many belts of wampum for confirming their words, held several councils at Detroit.

In his journal for August 27, 1765, Colonel Croghan recorded his speech at a council attended by Pontiac.

"Children Pondiac & all our Children the Ottawas, Puttewattamies, Chipways & Wyandatts," he began his speech.

"We are very glad to see so many of our Children here present at your Antient Council Fire, which has been neglected for some time past, since those high Winds has arose & raised some heavy Clouds over your Country, I now by this Belt dress up your Antient Fire, & throw some dry Wood upon it, that the Blaze may ascend to the Clouds, so that all Nations may see it, & know that you live in Peace & Tranquility with your Fathers the English."

Croghan paused and, to confirm his words, presented the Ottawa chief with a belt of wampum. After many more words and several more belts, the Colonel closed his speech with these words:

"Children We have made a Road from the Sun rising to the Sun setting, I desire that you will preserve that Road good and pleasant to Travel upon, that we may all share the Blessings of this happy Union. I am sorry to see our Children dispersed thro' the Woods, I therefore desire you will return to your Antient Settlements & take

77

care of your Council Fire which I have now dressed up, & promote the good Work of Peace."

The Colonel presented Pontiac with another belt.

At a council the following day, a sad one for Indians, Pontiac replied to Croghan. His speech, as recorded by Croghan, began:

"Father We have all smoaked out of the Pipe of Peace its your Childrens Pipe, & as the War is all over, & the Great Spirit and giver of Light who has made the Earth & every thing therein, has brought us all together this day for our mutual good to promote the good works of Peace, I declare to all Nations that I had settled my Peace with You before I came here . . . ."

Pontiac declared that he had taken the King of England as his father and to signify that he wanted to live in peace he gave Croghan a large pipe with a belt of wampum tied to it.

He ended his speech with a pathetic plea:

"Father Be strong and take pity on us your Children as our former Father did, 'tis just the Hunting Season of your Children, our Father the French, formerly used to Credit his Children for Powder & Lead to Hunt with, I request in behalf of all the Nations present, that you will speak to the Traders now here to do the same, my Father once more I request you will take pity on us, & tell your Traders to give your Children Credit for a little powder & Lead, as the Support of our Familys depend upon it. . . .

"Father You stoped up the Rum Barrel when we came here, 'till the Business of this Meeting was over, as it is now finished, we request you may open the Barrel that your Children may drink and be merry."

If Pontiac ever returned to his "Antient Settlements," he did not remain long. A short time after he left the council at Detroit, he was living in the Illinois country, and there he died—four years after he had asked Croghan to open the rum barrel "that your Children may drink and be merry."

The exact manner of Pontiac's death has been disputed. Father Pierre Gibault, writing to his bishop from Kaskaskia on June 15, 1769, stated: "The famous Pondiac, while drunk, was killed at Tamaroa, by a Peoria about two months ago. It is feared that his death will kindle a great war among the Indian tribes."

The killing of Pontiac had unfortunate consequences for the tribe believed to be responsible for his death. A British frontier general reported in 1771 that Frenchmen on the Illinois River complained "that the death of Pondiac committed by a Peorie of the Illinois . . . had drawn many of the Ottawa and other Northern Indians towards their country to revenge his death."

[Probably at this time occurred the incident that gave Starved Rock its present name. According to legend, a party of Illinois Indians, attacked by Potawatomis, took refuge on the Rock and starved to death rather than surrender.]

Even before the defeat of Pontiac, adventurous Britons had wandered into the Illinois country, and some are believed to have opened a market at the Rock in 1760. Between 1764 and 1775, Thomas Hutchins, a native of New Jersey and an engineer officer in the British colonial army, visited the Illinois country several times.

At the mouth of the Illinois River, Hutchins saw "an agreeable and commanding situation" for a fort and he noted "the beautiful meanderings" of the river.

On the Mississippi, before he entered the Illinois, he saw less appealing sights—sad evidence of the wrecks that a century of contact with white men had made of the tribes Jolliet, Marquette, La Salle, and Tonty had found on the Illinois.

"Three miles northerly of *Kaskaskias*," Hutchins wrote, "is a village of *Illinois Indians* (of the *Kaskaskias* tribe) containing about 210 persons and 60 warriors. They were formerly brave and warlike, but are degenerated into a drunken, and debauched tribe, and are so indolent, as scarcely to procure a sufficiency of Skins and Furs to barter for cloathing. . . .

"One mile farther up the *Missisippi* than *Fort Chartres* is a village settled by 170 warriors of the *Piorias* and *Mitchigamias* (two other tribes of the *Illinois Indians.*) They are idle and debauched, as the tribe of *Kaskaskias,* which I have just described."

Capture of the village of Kaskaskia by General George Rogers Clark and his Virginians on July 4, 1778, near the end of the Revolutionary War, made the Illinois almost but not quite an American rather than a British river. Only after two treaties, one in 1783 and a second twelve years later, did the British give up all rights to the Illinois country. And after the new United States of America settled with the British, it still had to settle with the Indians.

9.

Five Kaskaskias Cross the River

On a hot day in August, 1794, General Anthony Wayne and his army defeated a force of Indians at the Battle of Fallen Timbers in Ohio, a few hundred miles east of the Illinois country.

At the Treaty of Greenville, signed a year later, certain small areas were reserved to the United States government to be used for fortifications. In the Illinois country were three of these areas: at Chicago, at Peoria, and at the mouth of the Illinois River. Every other square foot of Illinois land not actually in the possession of some white man was relinquished to the Indians. But the Indians did not keep it long.

The United States government had adopted a policy of buying land from the Indians and opening it up for settlement. In the early 1800's its agents were more interested in buying quickly than in buying honestly. Its most active Indian agent, William Henry Harrison, later a President of the United States, bought land from almost any Indian chiefs who would give title. He cared little if the land he bought from the Sauks was claimed by the Potawatomis, or if the territory bought from an isolated Kaskaskia band belonged to the entire tribe. He bought and he bought. But he could not buy fast enough to keep ahead of land-hungry settlers.

By 1809, when Illinois became a Territory, the Indians were aware that white men were taking away their chief or only means of livelihood. White men had made them dependent on the fur trade. Now white men, with their farms and villages sprawling over the ancient hunting grounds of the Indians, were destroying the fur trade.

On Tippecanoe Creek, a branch of the Wabash in Indiana, lived the great Shawnee chief Tecumseh and his brother, the Prophet. From their village, they were sending messengers south, west, north, and east, stirring up Indian tribes to resist land-grabbing by the whites. They resented the Treaty of Fort Wayne, signed in 1809, by which Harrison had purchased from a small number of tribes about three million acres of choice Indiana land for less than $13,000. The land was given to the Indians by the Great Spirit, said Tecumseh and the Prophet. It belonged to all the Indians and could not be transferred to the whites at any price or under any conditions.

The Potawatomis, Ottawas, Chippewas, and Kickapoos, who had succeeded the Kaskaskias and their friends along the Illinois River, welcomed the messengers from Tippecanoe Creek. Many of them opened their ears to at least part of the message of Tecumseh and the Prophet: land-grabbing by white men to be resisted; the dress of white men to be given back to white men; Indians living with white men to be brought back to Indian villages; Indians to cultivate the ground again, return to Indian customs, give up firewater, marry only one wife; eat no food raised by whites; give back to whites all dogs not true Indian dogs.

"On June 2, 1811, a party of savages fell upon a family named Cox, near the forks of Shoal creek," read an account of this period in the Illinois Territory. "There were present at the time but two members of it, a young man, who was instantly killed, . . . and a young woman, who was made a prisoner. With the prisoner and all the live stock stolen, the Indians followed a northward course for home."

The number of Illinois settlers murdered by Indians at this time was not large. But fear that the Potawatomis and their friends would be inspired by Tecumseh and the Prophet to commit other murders prompted settlers to hold a mass meeting in St. Clair County to discuss ways of protecting themselves. In a resolution addressed to Ninian Edwards, Governor of the Illinois Territory, the settlers recommended establishing three forts or blockhouses, one of them to be "in the seditious village of Peoria, the great nursery of hostile Indians and traitorous British Indian traders."

Within a short time, the three forts were built: one at the mouth of the Illinois River and one on the west bank nineteen miles above the mouth, in addition to Fort Clark at Peoria. The forts gave considerable protection to the settlers, and "few accidents were reported to those who 'forted' themselves."

Governor Edwards was convinced that murders and robberies in the settlements were planned in the Indian villages along the Illinois. Late in July, 1811, he sent Captain Samuel Levering from Kaskaskia with a letter to the village chiefs demanding the surrender of Indians who had murdered whites and the return of property that had been stolen by Indians.

At Cahokia, Captain Levering was provided with a boat and a crew consisting of eight oarsmen, a Potawatomi, and four other men. At Fort Clark, the Captain sent a message from Governor Edwards to Gomo, the Potawatomi chief most friendly to the Americans. With fourteen armed warriors, Gomo left his village (near present Chillicothe), twenty-four miles above Peoria, and, flying a United States flag, came down the river to meet the Captain.

Almost too readily Gomo assured Captain Levering that he would help find the murderers and recover the stolen property—at least he would give the Captain the names of Indians suspected of murder. Then, with a present of tobacco from the Captain, he returned to his village.

The following day, Captain Levering set out to visit Gomo in the chief's own lodge. He wanted to be sure of the chief's cooperation.

At a village twenty miles up the river, his boatmen refused to go farther. Night was falling and, they said, they had not been hired to work after dark. In a canoe paddled by two Indians, Levering and his interpreter, Fournier, journeyed four miles farther up river to a creek. There they left the canoe and walked through "a moist and thicketty bottom" to Gomo's village.

The hour was late, eleven o'clock. Gomo and his people were asleep. But, when the chief learned that visitors had arrived, he cordially invited them into his lodge.

Gomo's wife roused herself and cooked for the guests a dish made from new corn. While Levering and Fournier ate, Gomo sat without speaking, smoking his pipe. Gathered about two fires near the center of the lodge, Indian warriors squatted in respectful silence.

When Gomo returned to Peoria the next day with Captain Levering, he promised to call a council of Potawatomi chiefs and warriors to hear the Captain read the letter Governor Edwards had written to his "children."

Several days later, on August 15, the council assembled.

The Potawatomis had bad men among them, the Governor told the Indians in his letter. The bad men had killed two settlers, wounded another, taken one prisoner, and committed several robberies.

"My children," Captain Levering read from the letter, "now open your ears to hear my words, and let them sink deep into your hearts. If you wish for peace with us, you must do us justice. If you disapprove those murders and other outrages that have been committed, you must deliver up the offenders; for if you harbor among you such deadly enemies to us, you cannot be our friends, and you ought not to expect our friendship." The Governor had signed his letter, "Your affectionate father, Ninian Edwards."

The council met again on the following day to receive the answer of Gomo, who spoke for all the Potawatomis present.

84

"We have listened well to your information, and hope that you will give the same attention to our words," Gomo said to Captain Levering.

"I am very glad that you have come among us, and that you have delivered the words of the Governor to all the chiefs and warriors in hearing. I intended to have gone to see the Governor, but it is much better as it has occurred, that he has sent his talk here.

"You see the color of our skin. The Great Spirit, when he made and disposed of man, placed the red skins in this land, and those who wear hats on the other side of the big waters. When the Great Spirit placed us on this ground, we knew of nothing but what was furnished to us by nature; we made use of our stone axes, stone knives and earthen vessels, and clothed ourselves from the skins of the beasts of the forest. Yet we were contented. When the French first made large canoes, they crossed the wide waters to this country, and on first seeing the red people they were rejoiced. They told us that we must consider ourselves as the children of the French, and they would be our father; the country was a good one, and they would change goods for skins."

The British and the French, Gomo reminded Captain Levering, had followed the practice of persuading Indians to fight their battles.

"From the commencement of their wars, they used many persuasions with the Indians; they made them presents of merchandise, in order to get them to join and assist in their battles, since which time there have always been fools among us, and the whites are blamable for it."

The whites, said Gomo, kill the Indians' deer and bears. Yet if Indians kill a white man's hog or cow they are called fools or bad men.

He complained:

"Whenever the United States make the Indians presents, they afterwards say that we must give them such a tract of land; and after a good many presents they then ask a larger piece. This is the way we have been served. This is the way of extending to us charity.

85

"Formerly, when the French were here, they made us large presents; so have the English; but the Americans, in giving their presents, have always asked a piece of land in return."

The Potawatomi leader denied that the chiefs knew or could be held responsible for all the murders and mischiefs committed by their young men.

"If the whites had kept on the other side of the waters, these accidents could not have happened; we could not have crossed the wide waters to have killed them there; but they have come here and turned the Indians in confusion."

Gomo insisted that the desire of the chiefs and warriors was only to plant corn and pursue the deer.

Then he asked, "Do you think it possible for us to deliver the murderers here today?"

After Gomo had finished his speech, he laughingly said, "We have had long talks. Will not a little whisky enable us to sleep?"

A short time later he delivered to Captain Levering two horses that had been stolen. Another Potawatomi chief promised to return two more stolen horses to the commander of the Fort Dearborn garrison at Chicago. The two chiefs gave Captain Levering the names of Indians they believed had murdered white settlers and assured him that Governor Edwards should have no trouble in capturing the culprits.

The Captain left Fort Clark to report to the Governor and soon after died from the effects of hardships he had suffered on the trip.

Time passed. The Indians named as murderers remained free. And early in 1812 more murders were committed in the Illinois Territory.

Although Governor Edwards was aware that most of the recent murders had been committed by Winnebagos living many miles from Peoria, he insisted that much of the trouble had been hatched in Peoria or the villages nearby.

The Governor called another council, this one at Cahokia, and on

April 16, 1812, he met with thirty-five chiefs: Gomo and twenty-one other Potawatomis, nine Kickapoos, three Ottawas, and one Chippewa. Five months before, an Indian force gathered together by Tecumseh and the Prophet had, during Tecumseh's absence, been defeated by an army under William Henry Harrison at the Battle of Tippecanoe. But the Prophet's followers were still carrying messages to Indians on the Illinois River.

In a long speech, Governor Edwards told the chiefs that their Great Father, the President of the United States, had given them "many proofs of his love for the red flesh, and the red skins will always find him a kind protector so long as they act with pure hearts." He warned them against listening to "that great deceiver, the Shawnee Prophet," who, he said, had been hired by the British to tell them falsehoods and to raise the tomahawk against their white brother. He told them they had not delivered up the murderers, as he had demanded. He advised them against joining the Winnebagos in a war against the whites and told them he had reason to believe that others besides the Winnebagos had taken part in the recent murders.

"My children," he said finally, "let justice be done, let all cause of complaint be removed, and let us again live like brothers.

"My children, we do not want your land. We have more land already than we can use, and I shall neither propose to buy it, nor does your Great Father, or myself, wish to take a foot of it from you. Those who tell you to the contrary, tell lies and wish to deceive.

"My children, shut your ears against all evil counselors and comply with your treaty and you shall still be treated as friends and brothers."

The following day, three chiefs spoke briefly and told the Governor that Gomo would reply for all.

"My father, you have heard what my war chiefs have said," Gomo began his speech. "I will speak to you as the Great Spirit inspires me.

"My father, in this manner the Great Spirit has taught me to speak by giving me a pipe and tobacco, therein to make my father smoke."

After he and the Governor had smoked the pipe of peace, he continued his speech. He referred again to the selling and buying of land.

"My father," he said, "we have reflected considerably since yesterday. It is neither you nor I that made this earth, and the Great Spirit is angry, and we do not know what he will do.

"My father, by what I see today, probably our Great Spirit is angry, and wants us to return to ourselves and live in peace. What I now say is from the bottom of my heart.

"My father, you see many children have sold their lands. The Great Spirit did not give them the land to sell. Perhaps that is the cause why the Great Spirit is angry."

Gomo assured Governor Edwards of his inability to find and deliver the murderers, of his friendship for the Americans, and of his refusal to join the British.

"My father," he said, "I have heard the good advice of your speech. I never listen to any evil birds. I am for living in peace, and I will return to my people and rehearse them your speech."

In reply the Governor again referred to the murderers.

"We cannot find them and you will not punish them; what are we to do?" he asked. "You surely do not expect that we will let our people be murdered, without revenge. If you will not give up your bad men who kill us, we must kill as many of yours—and then we may kill the innocent, which we do not wish to do."

Gomo promised to "pay attention" to the words of the Governor.

Two months later, the United States declared war against the British. On August 15, 1812, a sad day in the history of a young country, one American force surrendered Detroit and another evacuated Fort Dearborn. Indians from the Illinois River were at Chicago to take part in the massacre of United States soldiers and their families leaving Fort Dearborn.

Governor Edwards, believing that other Indian attacks would follow the Fort Dearborn massacre, decided to raise an army, take command of it himself, and defend the young Illinois Territory "to the last extremity."

While assembling his small army at a camp near present-day Edwardsville, the Governor heard that help was on the way. Colonel William Russell with two companies of rangers had been ordered from Vincennes to join the Governor's force in camp. General Samuel Hopkins, Revolutionary War hero, with an army of more than two thousand mounted riflemen hastily recruited in Kentucky, was preparing to march up the Wabash to Fort Harrison (near present-day Terre Haute, Indiana) and then west across the prairies. Together, the three forces would "sweep all the villages along the Illinois River."

In late September, Governor Edwards and Colonel Russell, with their combined forces of about four hundred mounted volunteers, left camp and headed their horses in the direction of the Indian villages above Peoria. Before leaving, the Governor had instructed Captain Thomas E. Craig of Shawneetown to proceed up the Illinois River in armed boats loaded with provisions and meet him at Peoria.

In the small army of Governor Edwards rode three individuals who later became governors of the State of Illinois: Edwards himself (third governor), John Reynolds (fourth governor), and Thomas Carlin (sixth governor).

As the horsemen approached the Saline fork of the Sangamon River, they came upon two Kickapoo villages. They burned both. They then marched "with uncommon rapidity" toward a Potawatomi village near the upper end of Peoria Lake. In an early morning fog four or five miles from the village, the men suddenly encountered two Indians. The Indians made signs that they wanted to surrender. The captain of a ranger company raised his rifle. A man near him begged him not to shoot. But the captain had not left home to take prisoners.

Dust rose from the leather shirt of one of the Indians as a bullet entered his body. With blood streaming from his mouth and nose, and chanting his death song, the Indian shot and mortally wounded an officer who rode toward him.

The second Indian, taken prisoner after escaping a shower of bullets, proved to be a squaw.

The Indian camp was at the foot of a hill and almost surrounded by swamp. The Governor's guides, instead of leading the mounted volunteers down the hill as had been expected, led them into the swamp about a quarter of a mile below the camp, "and thereby deranged a plan of attack" the Governor had devised.

Spurring their horses, the volunteers rode into the swamp "with such impetuosity" that the animals slipped and floundered in the muddy water. Horses went down on their knees, catapulting riders over their heads. Horses and riders came up covered with thick, black mud. The Governor's horse plunged into a deep mud hole. Horse and Governor scrambled out dripping black ooze. Horses became mired, and men attempted to pursue the fleeing Indians on foot. Men as well as horses became mired. Weapons, blankets, clothing, and provisions were trampled into the mud and lost. But the men succeeded in killing between twenty-four and thirty Indians (the Governor's estimate). Probably, as the Governor had predicted regretfully, they killed some who were innocent.

After destroying the Indians' corn, burning their village, and capturing eighty of their horses, the mounted volunteers returned to their Edwardsville camp "with all convenient speed." Fearing attack by a large Indian force, they did not linger to look for General Hopkins and his army or Captain Craig and his armed boats.

General Hopkins and his Kentuckians were still many miles to the east when Governor Edwards' horsemen lit out for their home camp. Most of the General's mounted riflemen were untrained in military matters and some of them were more interested in hunting game than in fighting Indians. Their progress was so noisy and slow that they never came within sight of the enemy.

Rain dampened the spirits of the Kentuckians. Rations ran low. Accustomed to hilly wooded country, the men felt lost and depressed by the flat prairies, many of them black from fires set by Indians.

Four days out from Fort Harrison, the men became so rebellious that the veteran General called his officers to a council. He told them that, if they could find five hundred men willing to proceed, he would lead them to the Indian villages along the Illinois, while the others could return in safety to Fort Harrison. In less than a hour his officers appeared with an unfavorable report. They had found only a few veteran Indian fighters and some of the officers, including Captain Zachary Taylor, later a President of the United States, who were willing to continue the march toward the Indian villages.

Despite the unfavorable report, the gallant old General paraded his army, placed himself at its head, ordered his men to follow, and rode off westward in the direction of the Indian villages. The men turned the heads of their horses toward the east and rode off in the direction of Fort Harrison. Even a future President of the United States was powerless to stop them. Soon the old General wheeled about and placed himself at the rear of the rapidly moving column to protect against Indian attack on men unable to keep up with the others.

Captain Craig's boats, like General Hopkins' army, had loitered along the way and they did not arrive at Peoria until several days after Governor Edwards had left the area.

Exactly what happened during the five days Captain Craig's boats were anchored in the river at Peoria will never be known, so varying are the accounts.

Craig maintained that he marched his company through the village and, seeing the doors of the houses open, had "all the property that could be found" put on board his boats, as he "thought no men more deserving" than his own.

In the village lived Thomas Forsythe, merchant, justice of the peace, and, secretly, an Indian agent of the United States government. He and other inhabitants of the village, many of them of French descent and unfriendly toward the United States government, were away from home at the time Craig arrived. When Forsythe returned, he demanded that the property be restored to their owners. How much was restored is not known.

Early in the morning a few days later, Craig's men heard shooting in the woods near the boats. Craig later claimed that his boats were fired upon by ten or more guns and that he tracked the shooters to the village. The villagers claimed that the shooting had been done in a peaceful pursuit by seven of their citizens who had gone out at daybreak to hunt beef.

After making prisoners of Forsythe and seventy-five other villagers, Craig and his men set fire to about half of the houses. Then he loaded his prisoners on board his boats, took them down river, and, near the site of Alton, set them ashore in the cold November weather without food or shelter. Craig's action was referred to by an early historian as "assinine and criminal."

The following year, Benjamin Howard, who had resigned as Governor of the Missouri Territory to become a brigadier general, marched an army of fourteen hundred men across country to Peoria and then up the Illinois River to attack the Indian villages that remained near the head of Peoria Lake. Among the villages was Gomo's. Finding the villages deserted, the army set them ablaze and returned to Peoria to assist in the building of a new Fort Clark.

Under terms of the Treaty of Ghent, which officially ended the war with the British in December, 1814, the United States promised that the Indians should be given back the lands they possessed in 1811. In

1816, the United States established new posts at Peoria, Chicago, and other places in Illinois and Wisconsin. The British objected, pointing out that the posts had been built in violation of the treaty. But the posts remained.

The United States government put pressure on the Indians to sign new treaties giving up their lands. By the time Illinois became a state, in the summer of 1818, the Kickapoos were the only Indians holding title to land within its borders.

Many Indians, even those belonging to tribes that had sold their land, continued for several years to live in the state. In the fall of 1818, Gurdon S. Hubbard, on his way to St. Louis to collect pelts for John Jacob Astor's American Fur Company, rounded a point of the lake above Peoria and saw that Fort Clark, which had been abandoned, was on fire, just blazing up.

"Reaching it," he wrote, "we found about two hundred Indians congregated, enjoying a war dance, painted hideously, with scalps on their spears and in their sashes, which they had taken from the heads of Americans, in the war with Great Britain from 1812 to 1815. They were dancing, rehearsing their deeds of bravery, etc. These were the only people then there, or in that vicinity."

The men in Governor Edwards' and General Howard's armies had come from areas south, east, and west of the Illinois River, many of them from other states. They had seen the fertility of the land along the river. Back home they talked about it. In a short time, families from southern Illinois, Missouri, Kentucky, Tennessee, and Virginia were moving on to the rich land along the lower part of the river.

In April, 1819, Abner Eads of Virginia and Joseph Hersey of New York arrived with two pack horses at Fort Clark from the Shoal Creek settlement in Clinton County. They pitched their tents near unburned timbers of the old fort. Soon they were joined by five other men from Shoal Creek.

The seven men went to work putting new roofs on two partly ruined log cabins near the river and enclosing fifteen acres of land with rails left by soldiers who had been stationed at the fort. They broke ground and planted it to corn and potatoes.

About the first of June, Eads returned to Shoal Creek with his horses and two of his friends to move his wife and three children to their new home.

With their household goods in a wagon drawn by two horses and with their cattle trailing behind, Eads and his family headed across country to the Illinois River a short distance below Fort Clark. There at a trading post they found canoes and Indians. The wagon was unloaded and taken apart. Then household goods, wagon parts, and family were ferried across the river in canoes. The horses and cattle were made to swim across.

Although other settlers soon followed the Eads and their friends into the lower part of the Illinois River valley, settlement of the upper part came later.

When Henry Schoolcraft, on his way to attend a treaty-signing with Indians at Chicago, canoed up the Illinois River in the summer of 1821, three years after Illinois became a state, he saw "not a white habitation between Fort Clark and Chicago."

Along the lower part of the river, Schoolcraft noted the pale and emaciated faces of settlers who were victims of malaria or "the ague." He saw "females shivering with the ague, or burning with intermittent fever, unable to minister to their children." The dreaded disease, the cause of much suffering and many deaths, slowed down settlement of the valley. Settlers knew how to fight Indians but not the ague.

As the settlers increased in number and took over land that many Indians still regarded as their own, tensions grew. Indians reacted to the intrusion of whites by stealing their horses, breaking down fences, and occasionally murdering a lonely settler and his family. Whites retaliated by driving Indians, friendly as well as hostile, from their villages and hunting them down.

In 1804, a small group of Sauks had met William Henry Harrison in St. Louis and bargained away the extensive tribal territories claimed by all the Sauks and Foxes east of the Mississippi River. Under terms of the treaty, the Indians were to be allowed to live and hunt on the land until white settlers purchased it from their government.

Early in April, 1832, Black Hawk, a Sauk medicine man, and six hundred of his followers—men, women, and children—left their winter hunting grounds in Iowa and crossed the Mississippi River. They were returning to their old home near present-day Prophetstown on the Rock River to do their spring corn planting, as they had been doing for many years. Also, they were challenging the whites who had driven them from their corn land the year before.

John Reynolds, Governor of Illinois, who as a young man had campaigned against Indians, called out the militia. He feared Black Hawk would attempt to recover his corn land by force.

From white settlements in all parts of Illinois, young men answered the Governor's call. One of the militia companies that reported to the Beardstown rendezvous was from Sangamon County. It was commanded by a tall, gangling twenty-three-year-old named Abraham Lincoln.

Black Hawk appealed to the Potawatomis, Kickapoos, and Winnebagos for help. No help came, except from a few Kickapoos. With United States forces close on their trail, the Sauk leader and his band fled up the Rock River and into Wisconsin.

At the battle of Bad Axe, on the Mississippi, Black Hawk's band was badly beaten. Many of his followers who escaped across the river were slaughtered by a Sioux band. Black Hawk himself was captured by a party of Winnebagos and turned over to a representative of the United States government.

Black Hawk, a powerful medicine man of the Sauk tribe and leader in the last major effort of Indians to regain their land in Illinois.

The Potawatomis had responded to Black Hawk's call for help by organizing a company of Indians to join the forces against the Sauk band.

The Black Hawk War, the final major struggle of Indians to hold or regain land east of the Mississippi River, did not touch the Illinois River directly. But five Kaskaskia warriors, among the last of their dwindling tribe that had once given hospitality to Jolliet and Marquette, passed through Springfield in June, 1832, and crossed the Illinois River on their way to join United States troops and take revenge on their old enemies the Sauks.

Even in the last sad and futile hostile action of Indians in the Illinois country, white men were able to do as they had been doing for a century and half—use Indians to destroy Indians.

10.

The White Man Takes Over

The night before Abraham Lincoln and George Harrison started home from the Black Hawk War their horses were stolen. Mustered out of service near present-day Fort Atkinson, Wisconsin, Lincoln and Harrison walked most of the way to Peoria. There they bought a canoe and paddled it downstream in the Illinois River. At Pekin, they stopped for provisions. Overtaking a long raft, they were invited aboard to share a meal of fish, cornbread, eggs, butter, and coffee, their only hot food for several days.

At Havana, they sold the canoe, left the river, and set out for New Salem on the Sangamon, Lincoln with his long legs leading the way. Near the river, where the sandy soil was hot and dry in the July sun, Lincoln slipped back six inches at the end of each step, and Harrison, walking behind in Lincoln's footprints, found the shortened stride just right for his legs. Lincoln reached New Salem ten days before the August election of 1832. Before leaving for the war, he had announced himself as a candidate for the Illinois state legislature. In the few days left for campaigning, he made several speeches in his home community and one in nearby Springfield. Although he was not elected, his home precinct gave him 277 of its 300 votes.

Of the four successful candidates, one was the Reverend Peter Cartwright of the Methodist Episcopal Church. In the sparsely settled counties along the Illinois River, Cartwright rode the Bible circuit as Abraham Lincoln was later to ride the law circuit. As Cartwright relates in his autobiography, he had moved to Illinois "to get entirely clear of the evil of slavery" in Kentucky and Tennessee.

In those vigorous days on the frontier, ministers of the Gospel battled to keep their churches just as teachers battled to keep their schools. One test of a good preacher was an ability to march down from the pulpit, collar a rowdy, and throw him out of the church building without interrupting the sermon.

At a camp meeting held in Fulton County the year Black Hawk was driven from Illinois, "some low and unprincipled fellows" set up a huckster's shop with tobacco, cakes, candies, pies, "and almost all kinds of ardent spirits." Knowing the effect of ardent spirits on rowdies who delighted in breaking up camp meetings, Cartwright asked the huckster to stop selling his wares. When the huckster refused, Cartwright had him arrested and tried.

Convicted by a jury and fined ten dollars and costs, the huckster refused to pay. He had no money, he said. Cartwright insisted that the huckster pay the fine or go to jail. The local law enforcement officer hesitated—the jail was ten miles away. His hesitation became panic when members of the "black-legged gang," the huckster's chief customers, boasted that before their man could be put in jail they would rescue him and give a sound drubbing to the person or persons who tried to take him there.

Cartwright then told the officer of the law to deputize him and "four other stout men" he would select. They would insure the prisoner's safe lodgment in jail, he promised. Perhaps fearing the determined Cartwright more than the black-legged gang, the officer did as he was told.

After hoisting the prisoner on a horse, Cartwright and his four stout friends mounted their own horses and, "well armed with bludgeons," started at "a merry jog" for the jail.

The rowdies who had threatened to waylay them did not appear.

But the prisoner never reached the jail. As the party came within sight of it, he pulled out his wallet and paid his fine and costs.

Back at the encampment, the rowdies were in a mighty rage because they had been deprived of their ardent spirits. They rode up to Cartwright and swore that if he did not permit the huckster's shop to open they would break up the camp meeting. Cartwright told them to ride on—that he and his people "could whip the whole regiment" of them.

At the candle-lighting time for preaching, while the preachers were shouting and waving their arms, walking the platform and pounding on the pulpit, the rowdies were as quiet as a possum up a tree. They were so quiet and so well behaved that Cartwright ordered fires and lights to be kept burning all night and appointed a number of strong men to take turns keeping guard.

After most of the people had gone to their tents and settled themselves for the night, the rowdies began "their dirty work." At a distance they barked like dogs, howled like wolves, hooted like owls. Coming nearer, they threw chunks of earth at the tents and tried to put out the lights. The guard drove them off. Toward daylight, they came close again, clapped their hands against their thighs, and crowed like roosters.

One of the ringleaders stopped in front of the preachers' tent, crowed like a rooster, and walked on. Snatching up a burning stick from the nearest fire, Cartwright flung it at the retreating "rooster." Sparks flew as the stick hit the "rooster" squarely between the shoulders.

"Take him! Take him!" Cartwright shouted to the guard as the "rooster" jumped and bounded away like a deer. The "rooster" or "deer" was too swift to be caught, "for he ran as though the very devil was in him and after him."

Returning to the preachers' tent, Cartwright was warned by a member of the guard that rowdies were taking wheels off the wagons and carriages of the tenters. Through an opening of the tent, Cartwright saw that his own carriage, which he had roped to a sapling to keep it from being trundled away, was being worked on by a rowdy. He slipped out of the tent, snatched up a stick, crept up behind the busy rowdy, and swung at him, "not with much intent to hurt, but to scare him."

With his hat crushed down over his eyes from the blow, the frightened rowdy bounded away blindly, bumped his head against a tree, and knocked himself unconscious. When he recovered his senses, he was "as tame as a lamb."

"This put an end to the trouble of the rowdies," Cartwright recorded in his autobiography, "and afterward all was peace and quiet."

The Methodists were not the only religious influence along the Illinois River in the forty-five years Cartwright rode up and down and across the state. Catholics built tall-spired churches where forest missionaries had once preached to Kaskaskia and Peoria Indians. Congregationalists came from New England, many of them bringing a burning desire to free the slaves in all parts of the United States. From the South came Baptists, some leaving their homeland because they wished to be free of the wrong that was slavery. From several directions came Presbyterians, who remained divided in their attitudes toward slavery. Lutherans came, and Unitarians and Universalists. Episcopalians came and, though few in number, built Jubilee College, a few miles west of Peoria. Several other denominations established colleges in the Illinois country, for to them colleges were almost as important as churches.

Although probably less than half of the total population of the counties along the Illinois River ever set foot in church buildings except at revival time, many of the settlers from the East and South who had known church life back home felt the need for worshiping together. They did not wait for the building of churches but worshiped

Tall-spired churches that have risen where bark chapels once stood.

in any fairly weather-tight structures large enough to hold them. At one time, the courthouse at Beardstown was shared by three denominations each Sunday: the Episcopalians in the morning, the Presbyterians in the afternoon, and the Methodists in the evening.

Along with the Congregationalists, the Methodists, and the others, came the Quakers, or Friends. In the summer of 1837 came Sarah Wierman, a widow, and her three unmarried daughters, Amy, Sally, and Eliza. With them were Sarah's son William, his wife Susan, and their two small daughters, Mary and Esther, all Quakers. Susan was the daughter of Benjamin Lundy, New Jersey Quaker and abolitionist, who in his gentle way fought slavery in places as far distant as Haiti and went to his final rest in a Quaker burying ground a few miles east of the Illinois River.

Eliza Wierman kept a diary of the twenty-day trip by canal boat, steam train, river steamer, and carriage or wagon from the old home near York Springs, Pennsylvania, to the new home on Clear Creek in little Putnam County, which straddles the Illinois River above Peoria.

Aboard the steamboat *Flora* on the Ohio River, Eliza imagined that the steam sounded like some great animal puffing and blowing. Arriving at the Mississippi River, the *Flora* turned upstream.

At the mouth of the Illinois, the *Flora* turned into the river that many years before had greatly shortened the way of Jolliet and Marquette. In the years between the coming of the first Frenchmen and the coming of Eliza, much water had flowed in the channel of the Illinois, much violence had been committed along its banks, many changes had taken place in the land bordering the river. The violence to the river itself was to be greater in the century after Eliza's coming than in the nearly two centuries before.

Under date of June 17, 1837, Eliza Wierman wrote in her diary: "We are now on the Illinois river; have passed two little towns in Illinois. The name of one is Naples. There are some good buildings

Peoria in 1832. This village looked much like several other villages along the Illinois River in the early days of the steamboat.

here. Illinois River is a beautiful clear stream, different from what I had expected."

On June 18, Eliza wrote: "This morning we leave the 'Flora' at Peoria and go on board the 'Frontier' for Hennepin. Capt. Burt of the 'Flora' says it is about forty miles to Hennepin. There is extensive prairie along the river. We have passed one village called Rome. The boat we are on now is a very pleasant one and we have very good accommodations.

"We landed at Hennepin after dinner today. The people all came down to the shore to see us land, but instead of 'a word of friendship and extended hands' we met only the gaze of strangers, in a place where we had no home to rest in after so long a journey."

The gaze of some of the strangers soon turned to kindness, and the Wiermans were shown to a hotel. There the Wiermen women and girls waited until William found a man who agreed to take them and some of their belongings in a wagon eleven miles across country to their friends the Lewises.

"It was prairie nearly all the way, with the best looking flocks of cattle I had ever seen," Eliza wrote. "The milk cows were fat enough for beef."

In stopping twice to ask the way, the Wiermans discovered two families named Hoyle. Like the Wiermans and the Lewises, the Hoyles were Quakers.

"They had heard we were coming and appeared pleased to see us," Eliza recorded in her diary.

Some of the Wiermans spent the first night with the family of Joseph Hoyle and some with the Lewises. Two days later, William Wierman and William Lewis went with a wagon and team to Hennepin for the rest of the Wierman belongings.

"It is agreeable to meet with Friends again," Eliza wrote, "but the route we came is ill-calculated to make us pleased with a new country thinly settled. Being in towns and crowded boats all the way it makes me feel lonesome here."

The Wiermans, the Hoyles, and the Lewises of Putnam County were part of a new movement away from the tree-lined Illinois River and its tree-lined tributaries to the open, tall-grass prairies. The movement gathered momentum after the capture of Black Hawk.

White men had lived along the banks of the Illinois for a century and a half before many of them moved away from it to make their homes. To white men, as to Indians, the river had been a highway for transporting themselves and their goods. It had been a source of water for drinking, cooking, and washing. The river itself had given them fish, and the forests bordering it had given them game for eating. Also, the forests had given them wood for building their dwellings, for cooking their food, and for keeping themselves warm.

A few miles, in some places only a few yards, from the river was the prairie—in summer, a grass sea, so deep and dense that men and cattle seemed to drown in it; in autumn, a treeless waste blackened by fire; in winter, a white, trackless expanse where frigid, cutting winds blew day and night; in spring, a boggy morass that mired men and beasts.

To men whose lives had been spent in or close to forests, it was at all seasons a forbidding land. And to many who superstitiously believed that soil that did not grow trees would not grow crops, it seemed an unproductive land. Not until all the land along the river had been claimed by other men did settlers in significant numbers move out onto the prairie.

11.

A Time for Greatness

About the time the Wiermans moved to Putnam County, the Illinois River became an important part of the Underground Railroad—that mysterious road to freedom for thousands of Negro slaves trying to escape from the South to Canada.

Not really a railroad and not really underground, this freedom road had many conductors, engineers, and stockholders living on farms and in villages close to the river. At the risk of their own freedom and safety, people who maintained underground stations hid fugitive slaves in their homes during daylight hours, fed them, and at night conducted them on to other stations nearer Canada. Sympathetic captains of riverboats going upstream sometimes took escaping slaves aboard as deck hands, sometimes hid them in the cargo.

The Underground Railroad had three main lines in Illinois. All of them led to the Illinois River, Chicago, and finally to freedom in Canada or to quiet existence in some large northern city.

Most of the conductors, engineers, and stockholders were members of religious sects. Some of the most active were ministers of the gospel. While the timid and conservative clung rigidly to their pulpits and preached only the first great commandment of Jesus, "Thou shalt love the Lord thy God," the stout-hearted and concerned stepped down from their pulpits long enough to practice the second, "Thou shalt love thy neighbor as thyself." Unlike the preachers who justified slavery as ordained by God, they included among their neighbors any dark-skinned man or woman trying to escape the bondage of slavery.

All operators of the Underground Railroad were aware that in aiding the escape of slaves they were violating laws of their government. But they believed they were obeying higher laws—laws of conscience —which they considered more binding than laws requiring them to return fellow human beings to slavery.

Not only were they willing to risk fines and prison sentences by violating laws that violated their consciences. They were willing to endure the scornful glances, the cold shoulders, the whispered gossip, even the violence of their disapproving neighbors. Most of them were scrupulously obedient to all laws except those relating to slavery. They were the righteous outlaws of their time.

In a comfortable house three-quarters of a mile east of the village of Princeton, and seven or eight miles northwest of the big bend of the Illinois River, lived Owen Lovejoy. A native of Maine and son of a Congregational minister, Owen had come to Alton, Illinois, in 1836 to prepare for the ministry under his brother Elijah.

When the pro-slavery mobs at Alton threw Elijah's abolitionist printing presses into the Mississippi River and finally shot Elijah to silence his abolitionist voice, Owen was there. The death of Elijah did not silence the voices denouncing slavery. The number of voices grew and their volume increased. And Owen's voice became one of the loudest.

The Lovejoy home at Princeton, where Owen was minister of the Congregational Church, became one of the important stations on the Underground Railroad. In 1843, when Lovejoy had been at Princeton less than five years, he was brought to trial for aiding in the escape of two fugitive slaves. Lovejoy himself, though not a lawyer, took an active part in the trial, which lasted a week.

The pro-slavery advocates hoped the trial would reveal the young minister as a preaching abolitionist, a law breaker, and a criminal. They hoped it would send him to jail. But they were disappointed. Lovejoy was acquitted. The trial and acquittal brought Lovejoy to the attention of voters and helped to elect him to Congress in 1856.

Among the many Underground Railroad passengers who stopped at the Lovejoy station was John Bowen, who had escaped from his master in Missouri. Ragged and hungry, John arrived at the station in the spring of 1849. What happened after that was told many times by Bureau County historians and, as the years passed, with many variations.

Unlike most passengers on the Underground Railroad, John was in no hurry to continue the journey to Canada. The Bureau County historians agreed on that detail. They also agreed that John was well built, intelligent, and a good talker.

When some of the people of Princeton learned that John was a willing worker and handy with tools, they hired him for odd jobs around their homes. John became so busy earning money that he almost forgot he had not finished his journey to freedom.

One day, as he was mowing hay or cutting grass (the Bureau County historians failed to agree on this detail), his former master and another man suddenly appeared. With pistols drawn, they ordered John to surrender. Binding his hands securely with a rope, they led him, like a horse, toward the center of town on their way to Hennepin to take the boat bound for St. Louis.

Hinsdale Phelps had seen the capture and taken a shortcut to Owen Lovejoy's house to tell what had happened.

Going into action with his usual speed and determination, Lovejoy hurried to the office of Judson Waldo, justice of the peace, and swore out a warrant for the arrest of John's captors, charging them with riot or with kidnapping (the historians failed to agree on this detail also).

Before John's captors could lead him out of town, they were served with the warrant. They and John were taken by Sheriff J. V. Thompson before Justice Waldo in the courthouse.

By this time, news of the capture had reached most of the residents of Princeton. A large crowd—both anti-slavery and pro-slavery sympathizers—gathered at the courthouse. The antis were determined that John's owner was not going to take the fugitive back to Missouri. The pros, though fewer in number, were determined that he was.

John was represented at court by Lovejoy and two friendly attorneys. As soon as the case was called, one of the attorneys moved that John should be released, as the warrant applied only to his captors. While the motion was being argued, a pro-slavery man named Tallet rushed into the courtroom announcing he had a warrant for John's arrest.

Annoyed at the interruption and doubting the legality of the warrant, Sheriff Thompson ordered Tallet to leave the courtroom. Tallet refused to go. As the sheriff with revolver in hand moved toward Tallet, the courtroom erupted in wild disorder. In the confusion, the ropes binding John's hands were cut, and the fugitive was hustled from the courtroom.

The sheriff slammed the door shut, but not before Lovejoy and a few of his friends had followed John into the street. With his back to the door and brandishing his revolver, the sheriff refused to allow anyone else to leave the courtroom until he had made his remaining prisoners secure.

Directly in front of the courthouse, or a short distance up the street, John almost collided with a horse. (On several details at this point in the story, the Bureau County historians failed to agree.) Equipped with a lady's sidesaddle, the horse was tethered to a hitching post in front of the courthouse, or, hitched to a wagon, it was being driven along the street by Lovejoy's hired man. Wherever the horse or whatever its condition, John needed only a little urging to scramble up on the animal and gallop away toward Lovejoy's house. There he arrived safely but so paralyzed with fear that he could scarcely slide off the horse and crawl into the house.

Bareheaded and coatless, the Reverend Mr. Lovejoy sprinted along the street after John and the horse, arriving at his home ahead of a long, thin line of pursuers. Standing at the gate, he admitted his friends. All others he warned to keep back. Tallet, waving the warrant for John's arrest, tried to slip through the gate, but Lovejoy slammed it shut with such force that the intruder retreated.

News of John's escape had spread through Princeton as quickly as news of his capture, and a crowd soon gathered at the Lovejoy gate. At this point, Lovejoy called on one of his most effective weapons—his oratory. Standing at the gate, he launched into a long anti-slavery oration. The crowd listened.

Before he had spoken many minutes, someone yelled, "There goes John!"

The crowd stared. Out of the Lovejoy barnyard galloped a horse headed north toward Dover. Low over the horse rode a man with a black handkerchief (one historian insisted it was a black veil) covering his face. A few pro-slaveryites on horseback took out after him. Some historians said they caught him, some that they soon gave up the chase. But all agreed that the man on the horse galloping toward Dover was not John.

As the crowd went back to listening to Lovejoy's anti-slavery oration, the antis to cheer the speaker, the pros to heckle him, hardly anyone noticed an "old woman" with a sunbonnet on her head and a basket on her arm hobble from the Lovejoy house to the Lovejoy barn. A short time later, a buggy or a wagon drawn by a horse pulled out of the Lovejoy barnyard and turned north toward Dover. Some Bureau County historians said that the "old woman," with the sunbonnet hiding her face, sat on the buggy seat beside the driver; others that "she" was stretched out on the floor of the wagon and covered with empty sacks. All agreed that the "old woman" was John.

Shortly after Owen Lovejoy had arrived in Princeton, several members of his Congregational Church objected to having their preacher mixed up in politics—that is, anti-slavery activities. Some objected even to his preaching against slavery. But most of them approved. In 1843, they "Resolved, that we highly approve of the frequent presentations of the subject of Human Rights from the sacred desk, as a part of the Gospel of Him who came to preach deliverance to the captives and to set at liberty them that are bound."

After his election to the United States House of Representatives in 1856, Lovejoy continued to work for abolition of slavery and to shelter fugitive slaves in his home at Princeton. He continued to believe that "We ought to obey God rather than man" and in "the right and duty of violating human laws when they conflict with the Divine."

Accused by a fellow Congressman of stealing the Negro slave of a constituent, Lovejoy replied, "I never stole any of the gentleman's negroes—he never rightfully owned a negro. Every human being that God made belongs to himself against the universe. And, sir, if this committee wish to know . . . whether I help fugitive slaves, I march right up to the confessional and tell them that I do. There is no human being, black or white, that ever comes to my door and asks for food when hungry, or shelter when houseless, but receives it; and if the invisible spirit of slavery expects to cross my humble threshold and forbid me to feed the hungry or shelter the houseless, I bid that demon defiance in the name of my God."

When Owen Lovejoy first met Abraham Lincoln, Lovejoy was too abolitionist for Lincoln to support, Lincoln not abolitionist enough for Lovejoy to follow. While Lovejoy wanted to abolish slavery, Lincoln at that time wanted only to stop the spread of slavery into new territories and states.

Then, on a stifling hot day early in October, 1854, Lincoln stood on a platform in a packed hall of the Illinois state house in Springfield and for more than three hours replied to a speech Stephen A. Douglas had made the day before. Douglas had argued for allowing the extension of slavery into Nebraska. With his coat, collar, and tie tossed aside, and with his shirt wet with sweat, Lincoln flung back his tousled head and demanded to know if a Negro should not be treated like other men.

"When the white man governs himself," he said, "that is self-government; but when he governs himself and also governs *another* man, that is more than self-government—that is despotism. If a Negro is a *man*, why then my ancient faith teaches me that 'all men are created equal', and that there can be no moral right in connection with one man's making a slave of another."

Hearing those words, Owen Lovejoy and his abolitionist friends tried to persuade Lincoln to join them in forming the new and radical Republican party. But Lincoln was not ready then. He was not ready the next year, either.

"Just now," Lincoln replied to one of Lovejoy's letters, "I fear to do anything, lest I do wrong."

As the two men became better acquainted, they gained greater respect for each other and came closer together in their thinking. They endorsed the same candidates for President of the United States and for Governor of Illinois. They spoke from the same platforms. At a Fourth of July Republican rally at Princeton in 1856, they addressed a crowd that Republican newspapers declared numbered ten thousand people. By that time, Lincoln was a member of the Republican party.

Two years later, when Lincoln and Douglas met at Ottawa in the first of their famous face-to-face debates, Lovejoy was there to listen. A few hours later, in the evening, when Lovejoy spoke at the courthouse, Lincoln listened. Then both men went home with the mayor to Ottawa to spend the night. When Lincoln arrived in Washington as President of the United States, Lovejoy was already there, in the House of Representatives. He was one of Lincoln's dependable supporters, and Lincoln was his friend.

In June, 1858, Lincoln had been nominated by Illinois Republicans for the United States Senate. In July, he had issued the challenge that resulted in the debate at Ottawa and seven other face-to-face meetings with Douglas, former judge and then United States Senator and candidate for reelection to the Senate.

Lincoln did not wait until he reached Ottawa to begin answering speeches Douglas was making in cities and villages along the Illinois River.

"Mr. Lincoln leaves tomorrow evening for Beardstown, where he will throw some of his hot shot into the Douglas camp, and charge home upon the doughface." Thus a Chicago newspaper announced the start of Lincoln's leisurely journey up the Illinois River toward Ottawa and the first debate.

On Wednesday, August 11, Lincoln took the evening train from Springfield to Naples, then the most important port on the Illinois River below Peoria. At Naples, he boarded the steamboat *Sam Gaty* for Beardstown and a political rally planned by his friends. Douglas had spoken at Beardstown the day before, and his meeting there had been large and enthusiastic.

The newly organized Republicans of Cass County worked hard to make their rally for Lincoln even larger and noisier. On Thursday morning, when the *Sam Gaty* with Lincoln aboard whistled for a landing at Beardstown, two brass bands, forty men on horseback, and a long procession of people on foot were there to meet him.

A Chicago newspaper reporter who traveled with Lincoln wrote that the address was one of the candidate's best.

The following morning, Mr. Lincoln, accompanied by many friends, boarded the steamboat *Editor* for Havana. He was in good spirits and he spent the trip talking politics and telling stories.

"From the beginning to the end of our travels," wrote the reporter, "the fund of anecdotes never failed, and, wherever he happened to be, all the people within earshot would begin to work their way up to this inimitable storyteller. His stories were always *apropos* of something going on, and oftenest related to things that had happened in his own neighborhood. He was constantly being reminded of one, and, when he told it, his facial expression was so irresistibly comic that the bystanders generally exploded in laughter before he reached what he called the 'nub' of it."

When the steamboat *Editor* arrived in Havana on Friday afternoon, Douglas was addressing a political rally, and Lincoln strolled over to the meeting in time to hear the last of the speech.

Lincoln's friends were indignant because Douglas had called their candidate "a liar, a coward, a wretch, and a sneak."

Those were harsh words, even in the heat of a political campaign in a state that had been a state for only forty years. Usually, they were fighting words. When Lincoln began his reply to Douglas the following day, he took notice of them. But he declined to accept the words as a challenge to fight. He gave two reasons: the first was that a fight would settle no issue in the campaign. It would only prove that Judge Douglas was a more muscular man than he, or that he was a more muscular man than Judge Douglas. The second reason was that Judge Douglas himself did not want to fight.

"He and I are about the best friends in the world," Lincoln told the crowd, "and when we get together he would no more think of fighting me than of fighting his wife." When Judge Douglas talked about fighting, said Lincoln, he was "merely trying to excite—well, let us say enthusiasm against me on the part of the audience. And, as I

Abraham Lincoln as a young lawyer and politician. (From a portrait taken in New York shortly after the Lincoln-Douglas debates.)

find he was tolerably successful in this, we will call it quits."

Having announced he would not fight Douglas, who was approximately a foot shorter than he, Lincoln went on with his speech. In the sweltering heat of the August Saturday afternoon, he spoke for two hours.

Delegates from Bath, a village eight or ten miles downriver, invited him to speak in their community the following Monday. He accepted.

At Bath, Lincoln found reminders of his early life and he shared them with his hearers. He called attention to some of the men on the speakers' platform—men who had served with him in the Black Hawk War. And he related that twenty-two years before, when he was surveying, he had with his own hands staked out the village of Bath in a wooded wilderness bordering the river.

Back to Havana Lincoln went, then to nearby Lewistown and Canton, and on to Peoria. Of Lincoln's appearance at Lewistown on Tuesday, a reporter for a pro-Republican newspaper wrote: "There are six thousand in and around the public square, at this moment, listening to Abraham Lincoln, who is quietly, coolly, but boldly and manfully discharging his arguments at the crowd."

Of Lincoln's appearance at Peoria on Wednesday, a reporter for a pro-Democratic newspaper wrote: "Mr. Lincoln arrived this evening and took rooms at the Peoria House—he looked jaded. I take it he has no hope—he is disappointed in the feeling here."

Saturday, August 21, 1858, in Ottawa was hot and dry. News of the first of the eight face-to-face meetings between Judge Douglas the Senator and Mr. Lincoln the challenger had spread throughout the state, throughout the nation.

From sunrise until noon, people poured into Ottawa. They came in wagons, carriages, and buggies, in railroad coaches, on canal boats, astride horses. They came singly, in pairs, as families, and as dele-

117

gations. People on horseback, people afoot, marched in procession through the streets, stirring up dust that rose in clouds, hung in the air, and half hid the marchers. Dust settled on banners and signs carried by marchers and on red, white, and blue bunting that draped the buildings along the streets and the speakers' platform in the public square. Dust clogged nostrils and, mixed with sweat, smeared faces and made eyes smart. Everywhere was noise, noise of brass bands blaring, noise of people talking, shouting, cheering; the measured noise of marching feet and now and then the sudden explosive noise that was the joyful abandoned roar of cannon.

Lincoln had spent the night before at Morris, on the river above Ottawa. On the day of the debate he arrived at the scene with a crowd from Cook and Will counties—a crowd so big it needed seventeen passenger coaches to carry it by rail from Chicago.

Plans for the occasion called for two large processions to escort the speakers to the public square. But the eager crowd had taken possession of the square, the speakers' platform, and even the board roof above the platform. For half an hour, officials battled the crowd, pushing here and hauling there, before speakers and members of the reception committees could be conducted to the platform. Just as the last of the dignitaries had pushed through the crowd to the platform and found their seats, part of the roof above the platform gave way with its load of men and boys and came down on the heads of the Douglas reception committee.

As soon as order was restored, the speaking began. Douglas spoke for an hour, Lincoln for an hour and a half, and then Douglas spoke for half an hour. Both speakers were interrupted frequently by cheers from their followers or jeers from their opponents in the crowd.

Douglas stressed the rights of the states to decide whether they should be slave or free. Lincoln stressed the rights of slaves.

As with most men of his time who knew Negroes only as slaves,

118

Lincoln believed that in many respects white men were superior. But at Ottawa he made clear to as many of the thousands as could hear him, and to hundreds of thousands more who in all parts of the United States read the newspaper accounts of his speech, that he believed in political and economic equality for Negroes.

In his high-pitched clear voice that carried not quite to the edge of the 5,000 or 10,000, or 20,000 crowding the square (newspapers varied in their estimates) he declared that "there is no reason in the world why the negro is not entitled to all the natural rights enumerated in the Declaration of Independence, the right to life, liberty and the pursuit of happiness."

Loud cheers greeted this statement, reported a Chicago newspaper.

"I hold that he is as much entitled to these as the white man," Lincoln continued. "I agree with Judge Douglas he is not my equal in many respects—certainly not in color, perhaps not in moral or intellectual endowment. But in the right to eat the bread, without leave of anybody else, which his own hand earns, *he is my equal and the equal of Judge Douglas, and the equal of every living man.*"

Great applause greeted Mr. Lincoln at this point, the newspaper reported.

When Lincoln left the platform at the end of the debate, half a dozen Republicans in a frenzy of enthusiasm, like that of a victorious football team, seized their hero and hoisted him to the shoulders of two of them. Then, behind a band blaring "Hail Columbia," they marched out of the square lustily shouting "Hurrah for Lincoln!"

A few days later, at Joliet, Douglas claimed that Lincoln was so used up in the discussion at Ottawa that his knees trembled and he had to be carried from the platform.

At Ottawa, on the day after the debate, Lincoln wrote to a newspaper editor in Urbana: "Douglas and I, for the first time this canvass, crossed swords here yesterday; the fire flew some, and I am glad to know I am yet alive—There was a vast concourse of people—more than could [get] near enough to hear."

In 1858, United States senators were chosen not by direct vote of citizens but by members of state legislatures. In the November election that followed the debates, and many other campaign speeches, the Illinois Republicans registered more votes than the Illinois Democrats. But the out-of-date apportionment of the time favored the Democrats; seven hundred fifty votes in southern counties, where Douglas was strong, were equal to about a thousand votes in northern counties, where Lincoln was strong. Of the state legislators elected, fifty-four voted for Douglas, forty-six for Lincoln.

The series of debates that started at Ottawa on the Illinois River failed to send Lincoln to Washington as Senator from Illinois. But two years later they helped to send him there as President of the United States.

12.

The Beast of Burden—
Before Harnessing

For hundreds of years before Jolliet and Marquette turned their canoes from the Mississippi into the Illinois, the river that greatly shortened their way had been carrying red men to and from their hunts, to and from their wars, and, when they moved, from their old to their new homes. It was a beast of burden. In the Illinois country before white men came, the rivers and lakes were the only burden bearers except men—and women.

Explorers who followed Jolliet and Marquette used the Illinois to transport themselves and their baggage. White men who traded with the Indians used the river to carry merchandise into the country and furs out of it. The early settlers who followed the explorers brought in their household goods, their farming tools, and themselves on the strong back of the river. They, their children, and their grandchildren loaded the products of their farms and mills on the back of the river and sent them off to market. Many of the needs or luxuries they could not themselves supply they brought in by the river.

As a bearer of burdens, the Illinois River did not have the same temperament throughout its length nor at all seasons.

Jolliet and Marquette entering the Illinois at its mouth in late summer, 1673, found it "broad, deep, and gentle" for about 175 miles.

"During the spring and part of the summer, the only portage is half a league," they reported (less than one and a half miles).

St. Cosme, canoeing down the Illinois in early November, 1698, found the river near its source a balky beast of burden. "We put all our baggage in the canoe, which two men paddled, while Monsieur de Tonty and ourselves, with the remainder of our men, proceeded by land, walking all the time through fine prairies. . . .

"After experiencing considerable difficulty during three days in carrying and hauling our baggage in the canoe, owing to the river being rapid, low, and full of rocks, we arrived on the 15th of November at the place called the Old Fort. . . . There we commenced the navigation, that continues to be always good as far as the fort of Permetaoui."

Henry Schoolcraft, canoeing up the Illinois River with French-speaking and song-singing voyageurs in a Chippewa birchbark canoe in the summer of 1821, found that the river had changed little in more than a century. White men had not lived with the Illinois long enough either to improve or to sicken it.

A trained observer and a faithful recorder, Schoolcraft saw at the mouth of the river "a smooth and sluggish current." He commented, "There is perhaps no stream in America whose current offers so little resistance in the ascent." The velocity of the current he estimated at a mile an hour or less.

The Illinois, where it entered the Mississippi, was about a half mile wide, Schoolcraft noted. From the mouth to the place where the river widened to become Peoria Lake, it was usually about three hundred yards across. But in some places the water spread wide over the low, flat land, creating false channels or lagoons.

The "beautiful lake of Peoria"—about twenty miles long and half a mile to two miles wide—was more attractive than the river below it, Schoolcraft thought. "The lake was calm, the air soft, and nothing but the measured strokes of the paddles, accompanied with the ever cheerful chanting of our men, interrupted the tranquillity which prevailed."

Above Peoria Lake, the river narrowed sharply and above the mouth of the Vermilion, "a fine clear stream," it greatly diminished in size. Schoolcraft and his voyageurs soon found, as Frenchmen had discovered more than a hundred years before, that in its upper reaches the Illinois was a balky beast of burden.

Half a mile above the mouth of the Vermilion, Schoolcraft's party encountered the first of a series of rapids. Only a few inches of water covered the sandstone rocks—many of them broken and jagged—that formed the bed of the river.

"When our canoe would no longer float without rubbing against the rocks, we got out and made a short portage, the empty canoe being still guided along by men walking in the stream on each side," Schoolcraft reported.

Two or three miles above the mouth of the Vermilion, where the water was in some places only eight or ten inches deep, in others only four, and where no deeper water was visible above, Schoolcraft and his voyageurs lifted the canoe from the river and camped near the Rock, which La Salle and Tonty had fortified many years before. From that point, they journeyed overland to Chicago.

The saddles that men put upon the back of the Illinois River for carrying their burdens before the coming of the steamboat varied widely in size and construction. The names applied to them were many; canoe, pirogue, dugout, bateau, skiff, flatboat, broadhorn, barge, keelboat, and such variations of one or another of these as Mackinaw boat, Kentucky boat, New Orleans boat.

No white birch trees grew in the Illinois country, and the birchbark canoes of Jolliet and Marquette were a novelty to the Peorias and Kaskaskias they met. Although birchbark canoes were brought to the Illinois River by later French explorers and fur traders, they were again a novelty on the river when Schoolcraft's voyageurs paddled their Chippewa canoe upstream. Schoolcraft's canoe was provided with a small mast and a square sail. It contained seats or places for six men to paddle, a place in the stern for a steersman, who stood while performing his duties, and space for a servant and cook, two passengers, baggage, provisions, and even books.

The wooden canoe or dugout (often called a pirogue) was the water craft commonly used on the Illinois when Jolliet and Marquette visited the Kaskaskias. It was made by hollowing and shaping the trunk of a tree. Some of the pirogues Jolliet and Marquette saw among the Peorias on the Mississippi River were more than fifty feet long.

Though pirogues were too heavy for long portages and were difficult and dangerous for the unskilled to handle, they were used in the Illinois country for many years after Frenchmen arrived with their light birchbarks.

Charles Ballance, who arrived at Peoria in the fall of 1831, found that white men there preferred making skiffs (rowboats of sawed lumber) to making dugout canoes. But he acknowledged that "the canoe was the better boat for the Indian and the backwoodsman. Those accustomed to them could run them with great speed, and were in no danger of capsizing them." Both the birchbark canoe and the dugout were propelled by paddles, with the paddlers kneeling or sitting and facing forward.

The boat that La Salle started to build at Fort Crèvecoeur in 1680 was followed by other craft somewhat similar to it. The bateau was built by the French, the keelboat by the Americans. Both bateau and keelboat were curved up and tapered at the ends, and both were equipped with oars, and sometimes also masts and sails. Sometimes on voyages upstream they were worked against the current by one of two methods, cordelling or warping, both of them requiring long ropes, strong backs, and tough hands.

The bateau, the principal craft used by the French for carrying passengers and freight on the Illinois River.

A trip downstream by bateau or keelboat from Illinois country to New Orleans usually required twelve to fifteen days. The return trip upstream was longer—seventy to a hundred days.

About the time Illinois became a state, the Phelps family of Lewistown had a keelboat built for their trade with the St. Louis market. They loaded their boat at Thompson's Lake, near Havana, with products of the countryside—with barrels of salt pork, dried venison, hams, and honey, with bales of deerskins and furs, with sacks of pecans, hickory nuts, ginseng, and feathers, with beeswax, tallow, and dry hides of cattle.

Using poles, oars, and sails in propelling the boat, they ordinarily made the run from Havana to St. Louis in four days, if the water was neither very high nor very low. They took at least twenty days for the return trip. They had to do a great deal of cordelling (walking along the shore and pulling the boat with ropes) and bushwhacking (grabbing the bushes on shore and using them to pull the boat upstream as they walked the length of the boat along the gangway or walking board).

The keelboat was not much used on the Illinois River until about the time Abraham Lincoln was born, and it was soon put out of business by the steamboat.

The flatboat had a different history, perhaps because it was easily made, cost little, and carried much. Common before the years of the keelboat, it was used for several years after the steamboat came to the Illinois River. A big, clumsy, square-cornered craft having no keel, it was difficult to steer. But it needed water only a few inches deep. Its crude cabin provided shelter for the crew. Built along the Illinois or its tributaries, it was loaded with local produce and started on a one-way trip downriver. Too heavy and cumbersome to be rowed upstream, it was abandoned at the end of the voyage, or it was sold as lumber to be used in the construction of buildings. Usually, unless the produce spoiled or was stolen by river pirates, the flatboat made a good profit for its owner.

People traveling in Illinois country in pioneer days sometimes had more difficulty in crossing the Illinois River than in going up or down the river. Not every traveler possessed the hardihood to cross in a canoe, swimming his horse beside him, as Peter Cartwright did on his way to a Potawatomi mission. And not every family had the skill, patience, or time to take a wagon apart, paddle the parts across the river in canoes, and put them together on the opposite side, as Abner Eads and his family did when they moved to Peoria in 1819.

At points where travelers often crossed the Illinois river, ferries came into being. Most of the early ferries were little more than log or plank rafts that could be propelled across the river by poles or oars. Where ferries were established, settlements grew or, where settlements grew, ferries were established.

When Thomas Beard settled on the Illinois River where Beardstown now is, he chose the location because he thought it "a valuable site for a town and a ferry." The ferry he built was just large enough to cross one wagon and two horses at a time, with little standing room for passengers. The propelling power came from a long pole in Beard's strong hands.

So profitable were ferries to rightful owners, and at times so difficult to establish was rightful ownership, that they were the cause of many lawsuits and at least one fight.

The early ferry at Peoria was claimed by two men, John L. Bogardus and Abner Eads. Bogardus had studied law (an advantage), but he had been raised in New York City (a disadvantage). Eads had never studied anything in books (a slight disadvantage), but he was one of the settlers who came to Peoria in 1819 (a distinct advantage).

Bogardus had got possession of the ferry at Peoria and, as he was collecting the fares, he was in no hurry to settle the claim of Eads. When sober, Bogardus feared mankind in general and Eads in particular. When drunk, he imagined that he had rats in his boots, that he was rich, and that everyone was trying to rob him. Sober or drunk, he carried a pair of small pocket pistols.

Eads, a sturdy, energetic, enterprising man, preferred fighting to

Ferry on Illinois River, about 1875.

lawing and one day, when he was wearing his heavy Mackinaw jacket with thick iron buttons bigger than silver dollars, he "walked into" Bogardus.

A Peoria historian recorded what followed: "In the melee, Bogardus was down, and Eads was on top, punishing him freely, as the bruisers would say. Bogardus, who seemed to be 'used up,' was all the time getting out a pistol, which he placed against Eads's breast, and fired. The bystanders, who were more the friends of Eads than of Bogardus, and who had not thought it necessary to interfere until the firing of the pistol, were at once greatly impressed with the duty they owed to Christianity and civilization, at once to stop the fight; and Eads, who thought he was killed, and Bogardus, who thought he had killed him, were easily separated. Eads did not wish to receive another shot, and Bogardus, believing the business sufficiently done, did not wish to spend ammunition on 'dead ducks.' Dire confusion prevailed. But when Mr. Eads's wounds were examined, it was found that the ball had not entered the skin: it had spent its whole force on one of those large iron buttons, and had only been able to drive it through the thick overcoat."

Ownership of the ferry was not settled by the fight.

The name of the first steamboat that puffed and chugged its slow way into the Illinois River has been lost in the gray fog of unrecorded history. On August 2, 1817, the *General Pike,* the first steamboat on the Mississippi above Cairo, Illinois, arrived at St. Louis. But several years may have passed before a steamboat turned from the Mississippi into the river Jolliet had called the Divine. The *Liberty* chugged up the Illinois as far as Peoria in December, 1829, and at least one steamboat had tied up at Naples, sixty-five miles from the mouth of the river, one or more times in 1828, or possibly as early as 1826.

The *Liberty* was soon followed by others of its kind. In 1831, Naples had 186 arrivals and departures, Beardstown 32, Peoria 17. In 1850,

59 steamboats were docking at Peoria, which had 1,236 arrivals and departures for the year, about 300 more than in 1847.

With the steamboats came changes in outlook, changes in the mode of living along the river. People of the Illinois River country now had direct water connections, much faster and much easier than they had known before, with Pittsburgh in the East, New Orleans in the South, and dozens of lesser cities along the way. They were freed from the sense of isolation imposed by arduous journeys between Illinois and the outside world.

In 1839, a man could travel in luxury as a cabin passenger the 223 miles from Peoria to St. Louis for $6.00. If he registered as a deck passenger, providing his own food and bedding, he could travel the same distance on the same boat for only $2.50. To ship a hundred pounds of freight from St. Louis cost him 25¢ to Naples, 37½¢ to Beardstown, 50¢ to Peoria.

For people living along the Illinois, the river became a glamorous Main Street. Not only did it help them earn their daily bread and supply them with such luxuries as they could afford. It brought them exciting proof of an outside world. Gleaming white showboats with their music, dance, and drama—*The Honeymoon, The Poor Gentleman, Uncle Tom's Cabin,* and *East Lynne* were some of the plays— gave sound, color, action, and make-believe to break the evenness of a work world that was monotonously real.

Each year when winter came and thick ice formed from shore to shore, traffic on the river ceased, usually for two, three, or four months. The ice that had stopped the canoes of La Salle and Tonty stopped the steamboats. Then life in the river towns turned quiet and dull, for in those days the towns and the people faced the river. They had not yet turned their backs on it.

The coming of spring meant the return of the boats. Even before ice in the river commenced to break into great blocks and float down

Illinois River showboat, providing music, dance, and drama.

with the current, piles of lumber and cordwood waited expectantly on the waterfront. Barrels of salt pork and flour, sacks of corn and wheat, bundles of furs, and other products of the Illinois countryside crammed the warehouses facing the river. And people in the river towns and the countryside began to talk about the return of the boats and to guess and wager which would be the first to tie up at the landing. Some people with baggage in hand arrived in the river towns to wait impatiently to board the first boat of the year.

No radar screen, no radio, no telegraph announced progress of the boats up the river. First news of the first boat of the year came when someone standing along the waterfront or on a high bank overlooking the river heard the deep exhaust of the old *Boreas*, the *Glaucus*, or the *Rosalie,* still six or eight miles down river. Advance announcement was unnecessary. By the time the boat came into sight, a crowd had gathered at the landing. A number of people anxiously waited to go aboard, some to begin their journey, others to meet friends and to learn the news from down river. Some people merely stood, transfixed in wonder at the splendor and the intricate architecture of the boat, the power in the deep-throated engine, or the bluff magnificence of the captain, especially if he wore white kid gloves while on duty.

When the Edward Collins family moved to Beardstown in December, 1836, eight years after the first arrival of a steamboat at Peoria, the boats had scanty accommodations for passengers. The deck of the *Wyoming*, the boat that carried the Collins family, was one large room, and each family aboard was allowed space for its members and their baggage. The Collins family had its own provisions and clean straw beds. One of the families on the boat had a stove, which the Collins were invited to use for cooking their meals.

Large cakes of ice floated in the river, and the steamboat moved cautiously ahead. Deck hands stood at the bow of the boat and with long poles tipped with sharp spikes pushed away the floating cakes.

When darkness came, cakes of ice sometimes banged against the boat, causing among the passengers a terror long remembered by one of the young members of the Collins family. As an old man, he recalled that each time a large cake of ice struck the boat "every timber would shake and shiver." He recalled the loud voices and the great excitement aboard the boat that night, and the anxiety of his mother who, holding him close to her, exclaimed again and again, "Another blow like that and we are gone."

In June, 1838, Abner Jones waited forty-eight hours at Alton for a steamboat that would take him up the Illinois River. Many northbound boats had passed, all of them continuing up the Mississippi or into the Missouri, when, late in the evening, the *Ashley*, crowded with passengers and loaded to the guard rails with freight, coasted in to the landing. A new boat, the *Ashley* was a regular packet plying between St. Louis and Peru, once a week each way.

All the berths were occupied. But Abner and several other travelers crowded aboard, knowing they would have to take their chances with sixty other passengers at "rough-and-tumble" on the cabin floor. By "a little management," Abner found a snug corner where, with his saddle bags for a pillow, he "passed a tolerable night."

At Naples, Abner watched the landing of two North Carolina families who were going to a tract of land they had purchased near Jacksonville. Among their possessions were two spirited bay horses (one of which fell overboard while being landed), a barouche, a buggy, four farm wagons, a large amount of "household stuff" (which included a piano and other luxuries), and groceries enough to last a year. Not all families moving into Illinois were poor immigrants.

When Mrs. Eliza Steele of New York City made a journey to the West in the summer of 1840, steamboats plied the Illinois only as far up river as Peru. A canal between Chicago and Peru was being built, she was told, and a railroad west of Chicago had been proposed. She and her husband would have to make the trip from Chicago to Peru by stagecoach.

After a day in Chicago, in which they were "able to see everything in and about the town," the Steeles "entered a commodious stage drawn by four good horses." At nine o'clock in the evening, the stage-coach with four passengers aboard started its trip westward. Shortly after midnight, the coach halted so suddenly that the sleeping passengers awakened.

Seconds later, Mrs. Steele saw the coachman with a lantern in his hand walking about on the ground, apparently searching for something.

"Halo, driver, what have you lost?" called out one of the passengers.

"Only my road, sir," the driver replied.

Soon the driver discovered signs of a road on the flat prairie, resumed his seat on the coach, and informed his passengers he had gone three miles out of his way.

Farther along, the stage stopped at a small house, where the driver awakened the owner. After refreshments for driver and passengers and a change of horses, the stage went on its way again.

At Peru, Mrs. Steele and her husband left the stage and boarded the steamboat *Frontier*.

"Fatigued as we were," Mrs. Steele wrote to a friend, "we could not leave the deck for some time, for the *night sun*, as the Indians call the moon, was shining brightly down upon the smooth surface of the Illinois, lighting up her forest glades as we passed, and throwing fantastic shadows over the silver water. However, a night and a day in a stage coach has beaten all romance out of us, and we at length retreated to our snug state-room. The mosquitoe nets were drawn over us, and we soon bid to nature and to you a fair good-night."

During the night, a heavy fog settled down over the river, and Mrs. Steele learned the next morning that the *Frontier* would be several hours late in reaching Peoria. After breakfast, when the fog had lifted, she went with notebook in hand to one of the decks, seated herself, and jotted down her impressions of the passing shore. Although she saw "no villa, or ruins, or lordly mansion to embellish the scenery," such as she might have known in Europe, she thought the forests along the Illinois were loveliness enough. She "gazed into the forest's deep recesses," noted the "long vistas through which the early morning sun was streaming," saw "the silvery barked white maple, its bright green leaves turning up their silver lining to the breeze," and the willow, "dipping its leaves in the stream."

At Peoria, Mrs. Steele and her husband left the *Frontier* and the following day boarded the *Home* for Alton. When they registered on the *Home*, they were requested to write their names, place of residence, expected destination—and politics.

On a piece of framed pink satin hung on the wall, they read the rules of the boat: no gentleman to go to table without his coat on or with any garb to disturb the company; no gentleman to pencil-work or otherwise injure the furniture (this rule referred to a popular pasttime, whittling); no gentleman to lie down in his berth with his boots on.

At Pekin, the *Home* stopped to take on freight, and the Steeles left the boat and walked about the town, noted especially the office of the *Tazewell Telegraph,* bought a green gauze veil, and returned to the boat, where the hot sun reflected from the sandy bank. They waited impatiently as they watched barrels of flour, in seemingly endless procession, roll from the large storehouse on the bank down to the vessel. They waited while the barrels of flour, a hundred sacks of corn, and other merchandise were loaded aboard.

The captain of the *Home* was well pleased with so much business. He was having a streak of luck, he said. At the end of four hours, the vessel steamed away from the Pekin waterfront and chugged three miles downstream to the mouth of the Mackinaw River. There the captain had another streak of luck and the Steeles another long wait. The Steeles watched as bundles of freshly cut laths and staves and piles of black walnut lumber were taken from scows moored in the river and loaded on the *Home*.

Soon after passing the mouth of the Sangamon, the *Home* stopped to take on wood to feed its boiler. The Steeles "embraced the opportunity to take a sunset stroll in the forest," where they saw birds "skipping from bough to bough," turtles "romantically reclining upon the logs beside the water," and wild fowl and paroquets "chattering in concert with the mocking bird."

Beardstown and Naples were thriving towns, for the river traffic was good to them. Beardstown, Mrs. Steele was told, had 450 steamboat arrivals and departures in 1836. Naples had 9 in 1828, the first year of regular traffic to that place, 108 from March to June, 1832, and possibly twice that number in 1840. In 1839, the *Home* had made 58 trips between St. Louis and Peru and had carried 10,000 passengers, the captain said.

"We are constantly passing steamboats," Mrs. Steele wrote in her notebook.

As the *Home* churned out into the Mississippi River, Mrs. Steele noted that the "rapid tide of the 'father of waters,' presented a great contrast to the languid Illinois. . . . We looked a last farewell to the fair Illinois, upon whose banks, or on whose water we had travelled for four days and four nights, a distance of nearly four hundred and fifty miles, if we include the Des Plaines. The loveliness of the scenery all this distance merits the encomiums made upon it by the early French writers."

13.

The Beast of Burden—
After Harnessing

Although steamboats had come to the Illinois River in 1828 or earlier, and traffic on the lower part of the river soon became heavy, the rapids in the upper reaches left a great navigation gap between the East and the West. The beast of burden that had balked when asked to carry the canoes of Henry Schoolcraft and other travelers stubbornly refused to carry larger craft.

In the years before the steamboat, when hundreds of keelboats plied the Illinois as far upstream as Peru, people talked of harnessing the balky beast—of building a canal that would connect Lake Michigan with the navigable part of the river. The canal that Louis Jolliet had suggested building at the portage between the river flowing east and the river flowing west became a subject of wide interest to a vigorous young nation thrusting westward. In 1818, the year Illinois became a state, the United States Government persuaded Indians claiming land in northern Illinois to cede a tract ten miles wide along the canal route then being considered.

In 1822, Congress passed an act authorizing Illinois "to open a canal through the public lands to connect the Illinois River with Lake Michigan." By that time, people had begun to talk boldly about building railroads. Some of them estimated that, while the canal would cost four million dollars, a railroad over the same route would cost only one million dollars. Not until 1835 was the final decision made to build the canal. Construction was begun July 4 of the following year. Twelve years later, the canal was finished and open for business. The *General Fry*, the first boat to use the canal, made the trip from Lockport to Chicago on April 10, 1848.

The canal was 96 miles in length, 60 feet wide at the surface, 36 feet wide at the bottom, and 6 feet deep. It had 17 locks. The total cost was $6,557,681, and, to March, 1879, total receipts (chiefly from sale of land along the canal) were $2,000,000 more than the costs.

Building of the canal had brought into the area hundreds of people: laborers, engineers, land speculators, and merchants, in addition to home seekers. It had begun the process of turning sleepy villages into wide-awake young cities. Many of the men who labored with picks and shovels spoke in languages or with accents strange to the river. Some came from Ireland, some from Germany, Sweden, Italy, and other European countries.

Opening of the canal brought into the area still more people— people who were looking for new homes on the prairies, most of them from New England and New York who had started their journeys westward on the Erie Canal. They were to change Illinois from a Southern-thinking to a Northern-thinking state. Hard feelings and bitter words went along with the change.

Most of the early Illinois settlers had moved into the state from Kentucky and other Southern states where living was more leisurely than in New England and had taken up land south of the Illinois River. Their easy-going descendants saw the canal as "a contrivance . . . admirably calculated for flooding the country with the obnoxious Yankees." They regarded every Yankee arriving in the flood as "a most ungenerous, despicable, cheating fellow."

The obnoxious Yankees retaliated by characterizing the typical resident of southern Illinois as "fond of dirt and ignorance" and aspiring to "nothing beyond the exalted idea of passing his life in a miserable, narrow log-cabin, with a squalid, ragged family around him."

Eventually, the canal had a pacifying, unifying influence on the state, for it encouraged travel. And travel brought together the culture from the East and the culture from the South. To the surprise of many people, the Yankee was not as despicable and the Southern Illinoisan was not as fond of dirt and ignorance as each had appeared from a distance.

In a five-year period, nearly half a million people were added to the 1850 Illinois population of less than a million. Most of them had boarded boats of the newly opened Illinois and Michigan Canal at Chicago. Many had settled along the Illinois River between Peoria and Chicago, the area in which Schoolcraft, on a journey less than thirty-five years before, had seen not a single white habitation.

On the busy Illinois and Michigan Canal, wheat, corn, and oats from Illinois prairie farms moved in boats traveling east. Sweet-smelling pine lumber from forests of Michigan and Wisconsin, store goods from Chicago and other cities moved in boats traveling west. Before 1848, much of the grain, lumber, and store goods to or from Chicago had traveled in creaking wagons pulled by plodding oxen or straining, sweating horses. In a short time, the canal made Chicago, rather than St. Louis, the favorite trading center for most of the people living along the Illinois River.

Many of the passengers on the canal—3,411,504 passengers in 1851 —traveled in packet boats. These boats replaced the jolting stages like the one that, a few years before, had carried Mrs. Steele overland from Chicago to Peru. They replaced many of the wagons that had carried families from old homes in the East to new homes in the West.

In 1850, the packet boat *Queen of the Prairies* usually made the trip from Chicago to La Salle in twenty to twenty-five hours. In its cabin, 5 feet long, 9 feet wide, and 7 feet high, ninety passengers could eat, sleep, and pass the time of day in comparative comfort. Their baggage was stored on the roof under canvas that protected it from inclement weather.

For the first few miles, the *Queen of the Prairies*, in company with other canal boats, was towed by a small steamboat. After the packet boat had passed the first lock, the steamboat was replaced by horses that walked along the towpath at the rate of about five miles an hour. Soon after the packet boat left Chicago, supper was served. Part of the meal, according to one passenger, was "the never-failing beef steak as tough as usual."

A short time after supper, male passengers were ordered on deck.

Log raft on the Illinois River about 1880. A boat was attached across the head with an empty barge alongside to fend off waves.

When they were allowed to return less than half an hour later, they found the cabin had been transformed into a sleeping room. Fifty "berths" had been created from three tiers of shelves arranged along the sides of the cabin, and twenty "beds" had been spread upon the floor. One end of the cabin had been curtained off as a dressing room for the ladies. The passengers selected their beds in the order of their ticket numbers. Because the night air was commonly supposed to cause malaria, the windows of the cabin were kept tightly closed. Some of the passengers awoke the next morning with severe headaches.

Traffic on the canal increased traffic on the Illinois River below. Faster, larger, and more handsome steamboats were built and put into service. The schedule between Peru and St. Louis was reduced in 1852 from seven to five days. But the days of glory for Illinois River passenger traffic did not last long. Five years after the Illinois and Michigan Canal was opened to traffic, the first railroad parallel to the canal and the upper part of the river was completed. Packet boats on the canal stopped running, and passenger traffic on the river declined.

By 1870, only four steamboats that carried passengers were running regularly between St. Louis and Peoria. Only one of these went farther up the river, usually to La Salle.

When passenger service declined, the Illinois River was not abandoned as a bearer of burdens. However, the character of the burdens changed. Today the river is still a beast of burden, less romantic than in the days of the canal, less conspicuous than in the days of the keelboat, less spectacular than in the days of the steamboat, but carrying heavier loads than ever before.

Charles Ballance, lawyer, judge, and respected citizen of Peoria, saw the change. Writing a history of his home city in 1870, he observed that about eight steamboats, called towboats, of a less expensive class than the passenger boats, carried freight up and down the river, "partly in their holds, and partly in canal boats and barges." Steamboats were too slow for passengers in a hurry, but not for coal, lumber, grain, and other heavy freight.

Towboating on the Illinois River was a gradual development. Not only were canal boats sometimes towed by small steamboats in the Illinois and Michigan Canal; they were towed in the Illinois River itself. At first a tow consisted of one or possibly several canal boats or barges trailing the steamboat. But rivermen soon discovered that they had better control of a tow lashed alongside or at the bow than trailing astern. To tow an automobile is to pull it. But on the Illinois and other inland rivers to tow a barge or line of barges is to push it.

By about 1860, the barges or the canal boats making up a tow were arranged in single file or two or three abreast ahead of the boat. When lashed together by ropes and cables skillfully arranged and tightened, the tow and the boat formed a rigid floating mass.

Eventually, barges replaced canal boats on the Illinois River. Traditional steamboats with their sharp prows were replaced by blunt-nosed boats built especially for towing (that is, pushing). With their four right-angled corners and straight sides and ends, the sturdy barges could be assembled and made into rigid tows more easily than the shapely canal boats.

Completion of the Illinois and Michigan Canal was followed in the next half century by efforts to harness the lower part of the Illinois River to make it a veritable canal. A navigable channel seven feet deep between La Salle and the Mississippi River was created by four locks and dams: at Henry, just below the great bend of the river; at Copperas Creek, a few miles above Liverpool; at La Grange, a few miles below Beardstown; and at Kampsville, about thirty miles from the mouth of the river.

In a few years, towboating on the Illinois River outgrew the seven-foot channel and its system of locks and dams. It had already outgrown the Illinois and Michigan Canal, which was abandoned in 1933.

People talked about a water highway through the heart of North America, all the way from the Atlantic Ocean, through the St. Lawrence River and the Great Lakes to the Gulf of Mexico. They talked about the Illinois Waterway as part of that highway. The Illinois Waterway would link Chicago and Grafton with 327 miles of nine-foot channel.

To give the waterway a channel with a minimum depth of nine feet required eight new dams and locks: five on the Illinois River, one on the Des Plaines River at Brandon Road near Joliet, one on the Chicago Sanitary and Ship Canal below Lockport, and one on the Mississippi River at Alton.

The Sanitary and Ship Canal, begun in 1892, had been in use since January, 1900, when the Chicago River that once flowed east into Lake Michigan was made to flow west and to carry Lake Michigan water and Chicago sewage into the Des Plaines River and then into the Illinois. The canal was deep enough and wide enough to carry most of the shipping that would use the lower part of the Illinois Waterway.

Each of the new locks was 600 feet long and 110 feet wide—much wider than the old and nearly double the length. A tow going up river through the locks would ordinarily be lifted 10 feet at the La Grange Dam, near Beardstown, and higher at the other dams.

In 1935, the Illinois Waterway was officially opened, although the last of the dams was not completed until four years later. Coal, crude oil, gasoline, sand, gravel, crushed rock, corn, soybeans, wheat, iron, steel, and other heavy freight moved up and down the Illinois in quantities the river had never known before. In 1945, the waterway carried 6,591,000 tons of cargo, five years later more than 16,421,000 tons, and twenty years later 30,812,773 tons. By 1960, the Illinois Waterway had become one of the half dozen most important beasts of burden among the rivers of North America.

On Saturday afternoon, November 20, 1965, the *Mark W. Rose,* northbound in the Des Plaines River section of the Illinois Waterway, tied up below the Brandon Road Lock and Dam at Joliet. The boat would have to wait until the *Leonidas Polk,* above the dam and southbound, had entered the lock, until the upper gates were closed, the water lowered, and the lower gates swung open to let the *Polk* through on its way down river.

The *Mark Rose* was not unlike many other towboats on the Illinois Waterway in the fall of 1965. Sturdily built, gleaming white and with bright red trim, it had at the bow four tow knees especially built for pushing and, surmounting its three decks, a pilothouse high enough to give good visibility of the tow and the river. It was 148 feet long and 36 feet wide, including the rubrails. It was powered by two 1,600-horsepower diesel engines that could churn the water white and push a tow more than sixty times its own weight. Owned by the Rose Barge Line, Inc., of Marseilles, Illinois, it had lettered on its stern "Wilmington, Delaware," its port of registry.

Its crew of eleven men consisted of captain, pilot, mate, four deckhands, chief engineer, assistant engineer, oiler, and cook.

In the pilothouse was a mobile telephone for talking to cities on shore and a two-way radio telephone for talking to lockmasters and to pilots of other boats. The call number was WD 2984.

As the *Leonidas Polk* with its tow left the Brandon Road Lock and glided downriver, Captain Oscar Elder at the steering levers in the pilothouse of the *Mark Rose* eased his boat and its six barges out into the channel and headed them into the lock, a man-made cavern with sheer concrete walls that rose more than thirty-five feet on each side. The massive gates behind the boat swung shut, and water from the river above poured into the lock. Slowly the rising water lifted the *Mark Rose* and its tow until Captain Elder in the pilothouse could look down on the top of the concrete walls and the red brick control house where the lockmaster supervised the locking.

The gates at the head of the lock swung slowly open. A short blast from the control house was answered by a short blast from the *Mark Rose*. Then the boat with its tow eased out of the lock and into the channel of the Des Plaines River above. Just ahead was the first of the six bridges spanning the river at Joliet. As the tow approached a bridge, Captain Elder jerked a cord above his head, and a long, low-pitched throaty blast split the airwaves and reverberated from the buildings that lined the river. In response, bells jangled and bridge gates went down, stopping traffic in the street on each side of the river. Each of the bridge spans rose to a vertical position and remained motionless while Joliet residents afoot and in cars waited impatiently for the tow to pass. A short distance above Joliet, the *Mark Rose* entered the Chicago Sanitary and Ship Canal, the upper section of the Illinois Waterway.

When the *Mark Rose* cleared the Brandon Road Lock on Saturday afternoon, it had in tow three grain barges picked up near the mouth of the Missouri River, two coal barges picked up at East St. Louis, and an oil barge from far down the Mississippi.

Before nine o'clock Sunday morning, the three grain barges and the two coal barges had been dropped off to be taken to Chicago by smaller towboats better suited to sharp turns in the canal and low fixed bridges across the canal. Within sight of the bridge at Lemont, the oil barge was tied off at a service dock, an empty coal barge, RBL 42, was picked up, and the *Mark Rose* was ready to head south in the bright sunlight of a brisk November day. Captain Elder turned the *Mark Rose* around in the canal with about two feet of clearance on each end.

Slight of build and young for a towboat captain (twenty-nine years old), Oscar Elder did not bark orders at the crew as riverboat captains are traditionally supposed to do. He gave orders casually, pulling down the microphone above his head and speaking into it in a conversational tone—almost as if he were talking to a neighbor back home.

Brandon Road Dam near Joliet.

Towboat and barges about to enter Brandon Road Lock (aerial view).

"Just leave that barge hooked there and we'll drop back and get that other riggin'."

"I guess we'd better tie the old thing off here. We'll pick it up comin' back."

Casual though his orders sounded in the pilothouse, they came through the loudspeaker to the mate and the deck hands on the main deck or out on the barges as the will of the Rose Barge Line, Inc.— the final decision as to *what* was to be done. By the rules of the river, *how* the what was to be done with the barges and the cargo was reserved for the mate.

Standing or sitting before the console, with a steering lever in each hand, the Captain appeared as cool as any wooded island in the Illinois. But beneath the cool was a tenseness that did not show through the skin. The captain knew well the capabilities and limitations of his boat, the value of the cargo, the vagaries of the river channel, and the possible penalties for bad judgment or lapses of attention at a critical spot in the river.

At noon on Sunday, Oscar Elder gave over the steering levers to the pilot, Ted Dean, who was as casual and informal as the Captain in the way he gave orders. Down below, the new watch went on duty and the old watch went off. Six hours on duty and six hours off was the schedule on the *Mark Rose,* as on other towboats, just as thirty days on the river and thirty days off was the schedule for the year.

A few minutes before four on Sunday afternoon, with Ted Dean at the steering levers, the *Mark Rose* left the Des Plaines and slid into the Illinois. By four thirty, the boat and its tow had cleared the Dresden Island Lock, just below the junction of the Des Plaines and the Kankakee. Over the broad river, much wider than in the days before dams, a fog was settling down. Trees edging the shores were reflected from the smooth, gunmetal surface of the river. The black square of mile marker 269.9 on the right shore was barely visible through the fog. Straight ahead, a reddish glow of the setting sun struggled to break through the top of a high bank of fog.

As dusk and the fog enveloped the *Mark Rose* and its tow, Ted switched on the two searchlights mounted on top of the pilothouse. Their powerful beams sliced through the darkness and fog as far as the nearest shore.

Ted pushed a button on the radar set at his right. The river showed as a broad, uneven, crooked ribbon of black; buildings, boats, buoys, and dry land as white.

Like other pilots on modern towboats, Ted depended on radar in a heavy fog. But in a light fog—"As long as you can see the treetops you can go," he said. "I've run the treetops down through here many times."

In the twenty-eight miles between Lemont and Dresden Island, the *Mark Rose* had taken on several empty barges. Ted did not like a tow of empties. "The wind blows the empties around," he explained. "But if you have, say, fifteen empties and you have a couple of loads you can do about anything you want with a tow."

Ted picked up the handset of the mobile phone and reported the fog to Lloyd Eneix, Port Captain of the Rose Barge Line at Marseilles.

"If the temperature changes, we won't have this fog," he said, "but if it doesn't change we'll have the fog all night."

From the left shore, where mile marker 267.2 showed as a red diamond during the day, a white light blinked feebly.

Ted tuned in the two-way radio telephone to the conversation of pilots on towboats up and down the river.

A voice on the speaker reported, "It's fairly clear around here."

Another voice, "I'll hold off a little and see what it does."

Still another voice, "It's foggy plumb down to Island Fourteen."

147

Feet sounded on the stairway leading from the second deck to the pilothouse, lighted only by the reflected glare of the searchlights. Don Carlton, the mate, stood in the dim light at the head of the stairway.

"Kinda soupy, ain't she!" he commented. He jerked his head toward the radar screen. "Old seein' eye workin' good over there!"

The beam of one of the searchlights held steady along the right shore. The beam of the other played nervously on the river.

The fog was no longer "kinda soupy." It was so thickly soupy that, by the time the *Mark Rose* reached Morris, Captain Elder had decided not to try to run through it. The *Mark Rose* needed some welding done down in the engine room, and welders who would work through the night were available at Morris. Before midnight, the following entries had been made in the log of the *Mark W. Rose* for November 21:

    12 noon.   Locking down Lockport Lock
    1:15p.   Dig out and pick up JIH 49   ADM Joliet mile 267
    1:40p.   Locking Brandon
    2:00   Dept.   Foggy
    2:15   Blockson   MBL 552 and 551 were not ready
    3:45   Locking Dresden Island 271.5
    4:00   Dept.   Wait NB tow clear EJE
    4:15   Dept.
    4:30   Running various speeds in fog
    5:30   Arrive Morris for pickup
           Off JIH 49 ADM (mile 263)
           and pick up LDS RBL 115-308 in dense fog
    7:20   Tie off at Ill Grain El to do welding while tie off in fog

Key to abbreviations: JIH, John I. Hay, a barge line; ADM, Archer Daniel Midland, a grain corporation; Dept., depart or departing; MBL, Mechling Barge Line; NB, northbound; EJE, Elgin, Joliet & Eastern Railroad bridge; LDS, loads or loaded barges; RBL, Rose Barge Line; Ill Grain El, Illinois Grain Corporation Elevator.

Wisps of fog floated over the river as daylight came Monday morning.

"She's liftin' a little," commented Oscar Elder as he studied the fog from the pilothouse. "I believe we'll take off here. We'll pick up these empties and then drop down and pick up those loads. Then we'll get plumb out of here."

While the tow, two barges wide, was being made up, Oscar stayed in the pilothouse, moving the boat and the barges and watching while the mate and two deckhands, Malcolm Pevahouse and Owen Neely, put on the fore and aft wires, the jockey wires, and the breast wires.

When the tow was ready, Oscar picked up the handset of the two-way radio telephone.

"WD 2984. The *Mark Rose* southbound at Morris. Checkin' for northbound traffic below Morris."

Back came a voice from an unseen pilothouse down river, giving the position and size of the tow and the condition of the weather. Oscar listened intently.

Then, "Okay, Cap'n. I sure thankee for that. The *Mark Rose,* southbound, departin' Morris. WD 2984."

The purr of the diesels down in the engine room grew to a rumble as at eight fifteen the *Mark Rose* moved out into the channel. In the light morning breeze, a small white flag floated lazily from the jack staff at the head of the tow. The flag would show the direction of the wind, and the jack staff, seen against the horizon or the river, would give a line of sight for guiding the tow down through the narrow rocky channel above Marseilles.

As in the days of La Salle and Schoolcraft, much of the river below Morris was lined with narrow belts of woods. But the vast prairies beyond the trees had been replaced by vast fields of corn. Indian villages that once faced the river had been replaced by cities and towns that turned their backs on the river and by factories and power

149

plants that used the river as a beast of burden, as a cooling agent for their machinery, or as a sewer for disposal of their waste.

In mid-afternoon on Monday, the *Mark Rose* cleared the lock at Starved Rock, passed on its left the massive rock that Tonty had forti-fied, passed on its right the flat ground where on a December day one hundred eighty-five years before La Salle had come upon the black desolation of a ruined Indian village.

At Spring Valley, where two barges loaded with corn waited in the river near a grain elevator, Ted rearranged the tow. More barges loaded with corn or soybeans were to be picked up down river. Putting the *Mark Rose* in reverse, Ted "twisted" an empty barge out of its place on the left of the tow, turned it loose in the river, ran ahead, and picked it up on the right, or starboard, side of the boat. The tow was now three barges wide and the empty was beside the boat, where it could be dropped off easily.

As the *Mark Rose* left Spring Valley, the red of a November sunset showed above a line of trees and spread along the western horizon. Gradually, over the river settled a darkness cut only by the beams of the two searchlights atop the pilothouse.

Far down the river, a dim light flickered above the trees, dis-appeared, and in a few seconds returned as a white glow that grew steadily brighter. Suddenly the white glow became two beams of light, one of them holding steady on a small white flag fluttering from the jack staff on the center forward barge of a tow, the other playing on the river until it picked up a buoy or mile marker and holding on that until it could pick up the next navigation guide. As the north-bound towboat came opposite the *Mark Rose,* the night seemed totally black, except where the powerful beams of four searchlights severed the darkness and where lesser lights glowed warmly from windows of the boats.

During the night, the *Mark Rose* stopped at Peoria to pick up other barges loaded with corn and soybeans. Near Liverpool on Tuesday morning, mallards and other ducks in their southward migration rested in huge rafts on Lake Chautauqua, beyond the levee on the left. A dozen wild geese plowed through the air above the timber where the Spoon River entered the Illinois.

A boat bound upriver with a long, low gasoline barge in tow came into distant view near the Cargill grain elevator at Havana.

"Which side you goin' to want down here?" the pilot of the other boat asked over the radio telephone after he and Captain Elder had exchanged call numbers and greetings.

"It depends on how fast you're goin'," was Captain Elder's reply.

"Come back again. I didn't hear ye."

"It depends on how fast you're goin'." The *Mark Rose* had been making a little better than six miles an hour.

"I gotchee. Okay."

For a few seconds, Captain Elder studied the channel and the speed of the approaching boat. Then he lifted the microphone to his mouth.

"If you want one whistle, it'll be okay with me."

A hearty "Okeedokee" came over the speaker.

Captain Elder pulled a cord above his head, and one long, raucous blast reverberated over the water and along the shore.

Men of the crews waved at each other as the two boats passed port side to port side. If the captain had called for two whistles, the boats would have passed starboard to starboard.

While billowy clouds floated lazily above two concrete grain elevators at Havana, the mate and two deckhands, Charlie Hendricks and H. C. "Deck" Decker, tied off more empties, picked up more loads. By mid-afternoon, the *Mark Rose* and its tow was again on its way down river. Fifty miles from a late sunrise, the boat headed into an early sunset with Ted Dean at the steering levers.

Ahead, at Beardstown, was one of the two railroad bridges on the

Illinois that, because of the angled approach and the narrow space between pilings, was a challenge to every towboat pilot on the river. Long before Ted could see the bridge, he had slowed the engines of the *Mark Rose*. He knew that, at the speed he had been traveling, he would need a mile of river to bring boat and tow to a full stop, almost that far to slow them to a speed that would put them safely on the other side of the bridge.

Darkness had fallen before the tow reached the bridge. By the beams of the searchlights Ted eased barges and boat between the pilings without touching wood.

Early in the day, Glen King, the cook, had made up a list of groceries he needed in the galley. He took pride in keeping the crew well fed, and he had not forgotten that Thanksgiving was the day after tomorrow. Captain Elder had called Glen's order ahead on the mobile telephone to a Beardstown groceryman who specialized in supplying towboats. By the time the *Mark Rose* had coasted to a stop in the darkness below the railroad bridge, the Beardstown groceryman was alongside in a small boat loaded with every item Glen had included on his list plus candy, cookies, and men's magazines that crew members had ordered for themselves.

When the *Mark Rose* approached the La Grange Lock less than ten miles below Beardstown, it had fourteen barges in tow: twelve loaded —three wide and four long forward of the boat—and two empty coal barges, one on each side of it. Nine or more barges meant a double locking; the six forward barges would go through with an electric winch on the first locking, the remaining eight with the boat on the second.

As the *Mark Rose* moved its tow toward the lock, the mate and two deckhands, lighted by the blinding white beam of a searchlight, walked slowly forward, single file, to tie off the first six barges. With their faded orange life jackets buckled around them, their hands thrust deep into pockets, and their shoulders hunched, they were the only moving objects visible in the chill night.

Early the following morning, Wednesday, the *Mark Rose* stopped at Florence, where a rocky bluff came close to the right shore. There the boat picked up more loads. When the tow moved slowly between the pilings of the old railroad bridge at Pearl with only a foot or two of clearance on each side, the boat had fifteen loaded barges ahead of it, five deep, three abreast, with more than 2 million dollars worth of corn and soybeans. The mate, standing on a barge at the head of the tow and giving arm signals to help Captain Elder guide the tow between the pilings, was farther from the pilothouse than the combined lengths of three football fields.

So solidly had the tow been put together with wires (cables) and lines (ropes) that it responded as a compact unit to every pressure on the steering levers and to every turn of the two wheels (propellers).

Some members of the crew, especially those with small children, had long faces at the thought of spending Thanksgiving away from their families. But Thanksgiving on the river meant Christmas at home.

Oscar Elder would spend Christmas with his wife and two small boys on his farm overlooking the Ohio River at Stephensport, Kentucky; Ted Dean with his wife and small son at his home within sight of the Illinois River at Kampsville; Glen King with his wife and forty head of Black Angus cattle on his 280-acre farm near Dalton, Arkansas.

Chief Engineer Ralph McPherson would be at Imboden, Arkansas; his assistant, Cecil Peck, and the oiler, Larry Leavitt, at Paducah, Kentucky. Don Carlton would be at Thebes, Illinois; Malcolm Pevahouse at Waynesburg, Tennessee; Owen Neely at Brookport, Illinois; Charles Hendricks at Versailles, Illinois; and H. C. Decker at Hardinsburg, Kentucky.

With Thanksgiving on the river at last an accepted reality and

Christmas at home a pleasant dream of things to come, the crew relaxed.

The chief engineer talked about old days on the river. He hadn't been there himself, but he'd heard tell of them. Most of what the crews had to eat, he said, was dried, smoked, or salted—dried or smoked meat, salt pork, dried apples, dried peaches, dried vegetables. But the milk was fresh. Just about every towboat had a cow on board —kept her near the stern.

The cook told about a towboat captain from Powhatan, Arkansas. The captain wasn't like other people when it came to cake. He wouldn't eat cake unless it had a topping of white soup beans.

The oiler told about one of his first trips on the river. The crew had watermelons for supper and had gone out on deck to eat them. After the fellows had eaten as much as they could, they got to throwing the rinds at one another. One of them had got a big collection of rinds and was slinging them at everybody that showed his head. Just as he let loose a rind with a lot of juicy red meat still clinging to it, the captain stepped out on deck. The captain got the rind right smack in his face—and the fellow that threw it got something else.

The oiler's story reminded another crew member of an oiler he had once known. "That oiler—he was a purty good little old boy. We was always playin' jokes on one another. One mornin' when I was a-sleepin' along about ten-thirty and the cook was makin' biscuits, that oiler snuck into the kitchen and got a wad of dough and rammed it into the toe of one of my shoes.

"Well, when I woke up, I run my foot into my shoe and there was that dough. It didn't hurt nothin'. I pulled my foot out and dusted off my sock and changed socks.

"Then I took the dough and run it right up into the toe of one of the oiler's good shoes—narrow, pointed shoes they was—and pounded it in. I knowed he wasn't goin' to wear those good shoes till he got off the boat, and he had a couple of weeks, or twenty days, it was.

"Well, when he got ready to get off the boat, he run his foot into his shoe, and there was that dough as hard as concrete. He had to take a screwdriver and a hammer to pound that dough out.

"He was a good little old boy, he was. We was always playin' jokes on one another."

In the thirty-two miles below Kampsville, the *Mark Rose* and its tow passed the remains of the old Kampsville lock, more rocky bluffs, more wooded hills, more pastured hills, more cornfields, more cottages along the shore, more grain elevators, several tows, the town of Hardin, and the Pere Marquette State Park.

Late in the afternoon, in the deep water near the Kipling Light at mile 2.2, Ted Dean moved the throttle of the *Mark Rose* to full speed. The engines responded, turning the wheels 280 revolutions per minute. The wheels responded. In the deep, wide channel below the state park, they kicked the water astern into white foam, driving the boat with its fifteen loaded barges smoothly and steadily through the water.

A short distance down river, the *Mark Rose* passed rocky dome-shaped hills that lined the left shore—hills that had changed little since the day Jolliet and Marquette saw them. It passed low-lying land on the right shore—a wild, wooded land better known to muskrats and migrating ducks than to men. It passed a wooded island on the right where a great expanse of water—the Mississippi—flowed around the island, joined the water of the Illinois, and flowed beside it until the two waters gradually mingled and merged farther down river. Three hundred miles and seventy-nine hours from the Lemont Bridge, it passed on the left the town of Grafton, where a mile 0 sign marked the official end of the Illinois River. It passed more rocky hills on the left shore and plowed on toward Alton and St. Louis—and Thanksgiving. Ahead in the dusk, the pea light on the jack staff of the forward center barge glowed dimly as a red dot.

Wildlife species that were once abundant along the Illinois River.

14.

Problems of the River

In the summer of 1773, long before the diesel towboat was invented and more than half a century before the people of Peoria saw their first steamboat, Patrick Kennedy started up the Illinois River in a boat rowed by several *coureurs de bois*. He was looking for a copper mine he had heard about. He never found the copper mine, but in his nineteen days on the river he saw a coal mine; he saw saline ponds from which the French made salt and a quarry from which they made millstones; he met with beautiful islands in the river and fine meadows a short distance from the river. He saw "plenty of good timber," "plenty of fish," "plenty of Buffaloe, Deer, Elk, Turkeys, &c."

Nearly a hundred years before Kennedy's visit to the Illinois, Sieur Liette, young nephew of Henri de Tonty, had gone on a five-week hunt with Indians living along the Illinois. "More than 1,200 buffaloes were killed during our hunt, without counting the bears, does, stags, bucks, young turkeys, and lynxes."

Schoolcraft saw mallards, black ducks, teals, and geese in great numbers the length of the river. He found deer common in the adjacent forests and prairies; an abundance of fish in the river—catfish, buffalofish, garfish, and other species "more esteemed."

From the crowded deck of the *Ashley* in 1838, Abner Jones looked over the broad valley of the Illinois and could imagine "no richer soil, . . . no greater variety of beautiful landscape."

Mrs. Steele, on her stagecoach journey from Chicago to Peru in 1840 saw "myriads" of birds and butterflies. She wrote: "A world of grass and flowers stretched around me, rising and falling in gentle undulations, as if an enchanter had struck the ocean swell, and it was at rest forever. . . . We passed whole acres of flowers all bearing one hue, as purple, perhaps, or masses of yellow or rose; and then again a carpet of every color intermixed, or narrow bands, as if a rainbow had fallen on the verdant slopes." She did not soon forget "that lovely purple evening" the coach journeyed between Ottawa and Peru over a road that lay beside "the bright Illinois."

William Cullen Bryant, New York editor and poet, on a journey from Princeton to Chicago in 1846, noted that the number of quail he saw along the way was "very great" and that still more numerous were the prairie chickens that swarmed in the stubble fields and in the prairies.

Kennedy and the others sang to the Illinois and its valley the song of praise that had been sung by Marquette and Jolliet—they had never seen anything like the fertility of its soil, or like its prairies, woodland, fish, and wildlife.

They saw the Illinois before many people had come into the valley, and with the many people its many problems. They saw it before most of the people in the valley had turned their faces to the prairies and their backs to the river and put the river out of mind.

Now the prairies are gone and most of the trees. The prairies were plowed up and trees were cut down. Pitiful remnants of the ocean of grass and flowers that thrilled Mrs. Steele struggle for existence along neglected fencerows and railroad rights-of-way. Trees persist on the islands and as narrow ribbons of woodland along stretches of the river, but in smaller numbers and smaller sizes than in the days before the Illinois and Michigan Canal disgorged its hordes of humanity into the valley.

Most of the marshes where waterfowl rested and fed and nested are gone. Gone are many of the floodplain lakes where fish in enormous numbers grew to astounding sizes. These were the lakes that brought anglers, including a President of the United States, hundreds of miles to fish them. These were the lakes from which, sixty or more years ago, commercial fishermen took buffalofish, carp, and other market fish by the millions and shipped them in carload lots to New York, Boston, and other large cities. Thousands of acres of these lakes bordering the river have been drained and turned into farmland by people eager to make money from corn and cattle.

Monotonous miles of levees built to keep the water from returning to these drained acres have fenced the river in, deprived it of natural storage space for flood water, and increased the possibility of flood damage downstream.

Where waving grass and bright flowers once made "a new and wonderous world of beauty," cornfields and soybean fields, factories and shopping centers, houses and office buildings and paved streets now encroach upon the river.

Once the tall grass and the prairie sod, the trees with their roots and their fallen leaves, held back and slowly released the water that fell from the clouds, the water that melted from the snow and ice. Now the clean-cultivated fields of corn and soybeans, the paved streets and parking lots, the roofs of factories, houses, and other buildings do little to hold back the water. Rushing toward the river, the water picks up and carries with it fine particles of soil, or silt.

The silt clouds the water, making life difficult for bass, bluegills, and other sight-feeding fishes. It settles in the river and creates bars that make navigation difficult for towboats. It settles in such floodplain lakes as remain along the river, killing plants and small animals that, directly or indirectly, furnish food for fish and waterfowl. It gradually fills up the lake basins, limiting the amount of water they can carry as overflow reservoirs in times of flood.

With the silt-laden water flowing into the river and its floodplain lakes go undetermined amounts of insecticides and herbicides used by farmers on their fields of corn and soybeans to kill insects and weeds. Scientists are only beginning to realize the effects of these poisons on the plant and animal life of rivers and lakes.

One of the problems of man is what to do with his waste material—the domestic waste or sewage from flush toilets, laundry tubs, and kitchen sinks, the industrial wastes from factories and food-processing plants.

When Chicago found that its sewage poured into Lake Michigan was making its drinking water unsafe for use, it remembered that the Illinois River flowed away from the lake. So the city built the Sanitary and Ship Canal and in 1900 began pouring its sewage into the canal, which flowed into the Des Plaines, which flowed into the Illinois.

For a few years, the Illinois River was not directly affected by the sewage from Chicago; the organic matter was oxidized or "digested" by the oxygen dissolved in the waters of the canal and the Des Plaines River. But, as Chicago grew and as other cities along the waterway poured sewage into the canal, the Des Plaines, or the Illinois, pollution moved downstream. By 1911, the upper part of the Illinois was heavily polluted.

The sewage, in its natural oxidation process in running water, removed from the water the dissolved oxygen needed by fish in their "breathing." It competed with fish for the available dissolved oxygen in the river. In this unequal contest, the sewage won.

Water in a river like the Illinois needs about five parts of dissolved oxygen per million parts of water to maintain a fish population attractive to anglers. In 1911, the Illinois River at Morris and Marseilles had a reading of less than one part per million, at Hennepin and Chillicothe little more than two parts per million. During World War

I and shortly after, partly as a result of war industries, pollution of the river was even greater. By 1923, Beardstown, more than 200 miles below Chicago, had a reading of 2.3 parts per million, and most of the readings above Beardstown were less than 1.0 ppm.

The people who hurt the Illinois River and its valley were by most standards good people. But they were thoughtless of the river or ignorant of what they did to it.

Stephen Alfred Forbes and Robert E. Richardson of the Illinois Natural History Survey at Urbana knew and understood the river. They had made scientific studies of it and its floodplain lakes. They had seen the river in its years of greatness. They knew how clear and beautiful the river had been, what quantities of fish and wildlife the river and its valley could support. Forbes' observations, begun in about 1880, covered a period of more than half a century. Richardson's studies were principally in the early years of pollution, 1913–1925.

After Forbes and Richardson had made known the extent of pollution in the Illinois River, the state legislature passed pollution control laws, and Chicago built sewage treatment plants. But human populations and industries grew faster than Chicago and other cities could find money to build the plants or legislators could find the will to make the laws.

Forbes and Richardson are no longer living. But William C. Starrett and Frank C. Bellrose, also of the Illinois Natural History Survey, now carry on studies of the river and its floodplain lakes in the tradition of their predecessors. Starrett specializes in studies of fish and the conditions that affect them, Bellrose in studies of waterfowl and their habitats. Both of these scientists were born in cities on the river. Both are stationed at Havana, in a laboratory close to the river.

Recent investigations by Starrett and Bellrose stand as constant reminders to city, state, and federal governments of the need for better sewage disposal, for practices that will reduce siltation, for a halt to the draining of floodplain lakes, for laws that will protect the natural environment of the fish and wildlife of the valley.

Will the Illinois River eventually become only a water highway and an open sewer? Sewage treatment plants built recently by Chicago and other cities have helped to improve water conditions in the river. So have recent state laws regulating pollution. But most of the dissolved oxygen readings in 1964 and 1965 were below the five parts per million needed for a fish population attractive to anglers. Starrett was less pessimistic in 1967 than in 1965 that solvable problems of the river and its valley will eventually be solved—that the people of Illinois will ultimately restore the river to some measure of its former greatness.

The river and its valley will, of course, never again be the river and the valley known to Jolliet and Marquette or Patrick Kennedy or Mrs. Eliza Steele—the river Jolliet called the Divine.

The "plenty of Buffaloe, Deer, Elk, Turkeys, &c." seen by Kennedy, the abundance of fish and the great numbers of waterfowl seen by Schoolcraft, the numerous prairie chickens seen by Bryant—none of these could stand up to the plow, the ax, the gun, and the flush toilet of the white man. The buffalo, elk and turkey are gone. The prairie chicken, gone from the valley, persists in pitifully small numbers in only a few Illinois counties.

The deer and the beaver disappeared from the valley, but they later returned. The wood duck was once threatened with extinction, but with the aid of man it increased in numbers.

Fish in enormous numbers will never again grow to astounding sizes in the river and its floodplain lakes, but both commercial fishing and angling can be improved if people of the state will act upon the information already available to them.

Waterfowl will never again be abundant the length of the river. But, during the fall migration, ducks and geese still rest and feed in large numbers on a few floodplain lakes and, with the knowledge already at hand, more water areas can be made havens where thousands of waterfowl find food and rest.

Pollution, siltation, and the pressure of human populations—these are the principal problems of the Illinois River and its valley. They can never be completely solved, because people are in the valley to stay. But the people can restore to the river some of the beauty and the greatness it once knew if they recognize that they create the problems of the river and that only they can solve them.

15.

To See and Do along the River

Unlike the Hudson and the Mississippi, the Illinois River has no highways or railroads that run within sight of it for long distances. So if you want to become acquainted with the Illinois you must see it from key spots that bring you close to the water or from the river itself.

Key spots include several state parks, state conservation areas, and federal wildlife refuges. They include also some of the villages and certain small parts of most of the cities that border the river. Visits to these spots will help you to understand the river as it is today and to reconstruct in your mind the days of canoes and pirogues, of ferries, of flatboats, keelboats, and steamboats.

Maps showing the location of the parks, conservation areas, and wildlife refuges, and useful information about them, can be obtained from the Illinois State Department of Conservation at Springfield.

Two of the state parks, Starved Rock, near the great bend of the river, and Pere Marquette, near the mouth, offer a wide variety of activities that will help you to know the river—camping, picnicking, hiking, boating, and fishing. Each of these parks has cabins and also a lodge with a dining room open to the public.

Three other state parks, Channahon, William G. Stratton, and Illini, all bordering the upper part of the river, have facilities for picnicking, camping, boating, and fishing. At Channahon are an old lock and lockmaster's house on the Illinois and Michigan Canal.

Buffalo Rock near Ottawa and Gebhard Woods near Morris are

state parks with picnic areas. Buffalo Rock provides several good views of the river. It was the site of one of the villages of La Salle's great Indian confederacy of 1683. Gebhard Woods is a pleasant spot at the end of a hiking trail along the Illinois and Michigan Canal west from Channahon.

The state park known as Fort Creve Coeur, near Peoria, has a monument to La Salle and a quiet isolation that will enable you to relive the day nearly three hundred years ago when a dreamer of empire found a deserted fort and a sign with the words *"Nous sommes touts sauvages"*—"We are all savages." Your enjoyment of the place is not spoiled by knowing that several historians believe La Salle's Fort Crèvecoeur was near, rather than on, the spot marked by the monument.

None of the state parks bordering the Illinois River lists swimming in the river as a recommended activity.

The state conservation areas along the river—most of them are indicated on state highway maps—are managed mainly for wildlife, but at specified times fishing, boating, and hunting are permitted in them.

Most famous of the federal conservation areas along the Illinois River is the 4,500-acre Chautauqua National Wildlife Refuge. Its headquarters are about nine miles northeast of Havana. At the height of the autumn migration period, great numbers of southbound mallards and other wild ducks—in some years more than two hundred thousand at a time—rest on 3,500-acre Lake Chautauqua, which is part of the refuge and is separated from the river by a narrow levee. On many afternoons, as dusk approaches, thousands of mallards rise from the water and fly out to feed on neighboring lakes or in cornfields several miles from the river. Small numbers of ducks stop at the refuge on their northward migration.

In spring, summer, and fall, wood ducks, among the most unusual of waterfowl, live on the refuge. The male, with his head of iridescent green and purple bordered with white, his burgundy-red breast, milk-white belly, and iridescent black back, is the most brilliantly colored of North American ducks. The female, modest brown in color, is an expert flier that nests in tree cavities or in man-made houses attached to the trunks of trees.

Canada, blue, and snow geese stop at Lake Chautauqua in autumn, and Canadas in the spring also. Throughout the summer, American egrets, conspicuously white against their background, and great blue herons wade and feed in the shallow water at the edge of the lake. Plovers, sandpipers, and other shore birds feed on the mudflats in summer.

In winter, bald eagles—as many as thirty at a time—feed along the river during the day and spend the night in the mature woods on the refuge. "They come with the ice and go with the ice," one ornithologist says. So spectacular are the big birds that bird watchers have driven two hundred miles to see them.

In the woods and fields surrounding the lake, many species of birds nest and feed and rest. The number of species recorded for the refuge as of May, 1967, was 246.

Rarer and shyer than the birds are the mammals that live on the refuge. Among the twenty-eight species that have been seen and identified are the coyote, gray fox, red fox, raccoon, opossum, badger, beaver, whitetail deer, and several smaller animals.

Plants in great variety and numbers grow in the lake, along the shore, and in the nearby woods and fields. Conspicuous in the lake are the lotus beds that provide hiding and feeding areas for young wood ducks.

The Chautauqua National Wildlife Refuge is administered by the Bureau of Sport Fisheries and Wildlife, United States Fish and Wildlife Service. Parts of the refuge are open to the public throughout the year. Arrangements for guided tours of small groups can be made by appointment with the refuge manager. Fishing is permitted in most parts of the lake except during the fall migration period. Attendants at automobile service stations in Havana can give directions for finding the refuge and its headquarters building.

Two other federal wildlife refuges border the Illinois River: a small one on the west side of the river between Henry and Sparland and a large one on both sides of the river near the Pere Marquette State Park.

The years that have changed the Illinois River have also changed the communities along its banks. But some of the villages bordering the lower part of the river have changed little in size and appearance in the past fifty years. And in most of the cities some reminders of the past persist, for even time does not erase all signs of the world that was.

Ancient buildings, weathered waterfronts, abandoned locks, stone monuments, bronze plaques, and old trees shading narrow streets and spacious public squares are all reminders of the past along the river. All of them are mute to the casual observer. Visits with local people having long memories will help to make them speak. So will county histories found in public libraries. So will articles published by the Illinois State Historical Society at Springfield and available in many libraries.

At Ottawa, the tall, imposing Reddick house stares coldly down on the huge boulder and the bronze plaque that commemorate the first Lincoln-Douglas debate. Built by William Reddick, abolitionist and friend of Abraham Lincoln, it has substantial red brick walls that once echoed to the tramp of soldier feet marching off to the Civil War. Long ago, Reddick gave his home to the city of Ottawa to be used as a library. In the library, you will find pamphlets and books that give tongue to the boulder in the park.

Near Utica, the Rock rises from the water as it did when La Salle and Tonty built Fort St. Louis at the summit. With a copy of *La Salle and the Discovery of the Great West* in hand, you can travel with the author, Francis Parkman, as he describes how he located the site of the Great Illinois Town near the Rock. With him, you can take a position on one of the hills north of Utica and look through field glasses south across country to the rocky cliffs and wooded hills on the left bank of the river. You will be able to see the cliff known to the French as Le Rocher, or the Rock, and to you as Starved Rock. Possibly you will be able to distinguish the gap in the hills where the Vermilion River (the Aramoni to the French) flows into the Illinois. With these landmarks, you can locate the site of the Great Illinois Town as historian Parkman describes it in Appendix I of his book on La Salle.

In the village of Utica, a monument to Father Jacques Marquette stands a few feet north of St. Mary's Catholic Church. The bronze figure of the Jesuit priest faces eastward toward the site of the mission he founded among the Kaskaskias approximately three hundred years ago.

At Peru, red brick buildings parade rank behind rank up the hill away from the river, much as they did when the waterfront marked the northern limit of steamboat navigation on the Illinois.

At Henry, one of the several river towns that have claimed to be the duck-hunting capital of the world, a picturesque pile of great stone blocks rises from the water to indicate where the first lock on the Illinois River was built in 1872.

At Peoria, no trace of the ferry that caused the fight between Abner Eads and John L. Bogardus can be found, no trace of any Fort Clark, no trace of the second Fort St. Louis, which was probably west of the narrows between Upper and Lower Peoria lakes. In the Peoria Historical Museum are relics of the past and a series of old notebooks that will interest the serious student of history. From Grandview Drive, on Peoria Heights, is one of the best views of the water that was once known as Lake Pimitoui. Sailboats are common on the water in summer. About two miles south and west of the town of Creve Coeur, which is south of Peoria and on the east bank of the Illinois River, is the Peoria Lock. Here visitors can have a close look at the barges and towboats passing through.

At the foot of Market Street in Havana, a monument on the bank of the river commemorates Abraham Lincoln's return from the Black Hawk War, and a plaque on a stone near the courthouse records that "Abraham Lincoln traveled this way as he rode the circuit of the Eighth Judicial District, 1847–1857." The courthouse Lincoln knew was destroyed by fire in 1882.

At Beardstown, the red brick building in which Lincoln defended William (Duff) Armstrong against a murder charge faces the public square as it did in May, 1858. The building is now a city hall rather than a county courthouse. It has a bronze plaque on the front as a reminder that a famous trial was held within its walls. But in other respects it has not changed much since Lincoln helped to clear the wayward son of his old friends Jack and Hannah Armstrong by calling for an almanac and showing the jury that, on the night of the fatal blow that led to the charge of murder, the moon was not bright enough for the state's star witness to have seen all he claimed to see. The story of the prominent Springfield lawyer who, in return for past kindnesses by Duff's parents, offered his services free has been told many times, notably by Carl Sandburg and by Benjamin P. Thomas in their biographies of Lincoln and by Albert A. Woldman in his book *Lawyer Lincoln*.

At Naples, a bronze plaque on a boulder under an oak tree within stone's throw of the river marks the place where the Twenty-First Regiment of Illinois Volunteers, organized at Mattoon and commanded by Colonel Ulysses S. Grant, went into camp on Saturday, July 6, 1861.

At the Pere Marquette State Park, a large stone cross commemorating the arrival of Marquette and Jolliet in the Illinois country overlooks Illinois Highway 100 and the river.

In recent years, the Illinois State Department of Conservation has encouraged boating on the Illinois River by establishing docks and launching areas. These places are shown on a special cruise map issued by the department. Roads leading to them are shown on Illinois highway maps. Any spot on the Illinois River with a good launching or docking area is apt to provide good boating. But for certain purposes some parts of the river are better than others.

If you want only scenery with your boating, you have a great number of choices. A trip downstream from Havana will give you a variety of island, lowland, and upland scenes; turn left into Bath Chute at the head of Grand Island (mile marker 113.3), circle Grand Island, and return in the main channel of the river. A trip between Florence and the mouth of the river will give you rugged cliffs and shapely green hills, as well as flat country.

If you want history mixed with your scenery, put your boat in the river at Ottawa, Peoria, Beardstown, or Grafton.

If you want fishing with your scenery, try your tackle on crappies, bass, or bullheads in Bath Chute, Twin Sister Island Chutes above Henry, the east channel of the river near Chillicothe, or Dark Chute at Godar Landing above Hardin. If you prefer bluegills, fish the bottomland lakes that border the river: Lake Chautauqua, Anderson Lake, Matanzas Bay, or any of the overflow lakes in the Grafton area.

If you are a bird watcher, choose the time of year and the part of the river most favorable for the birds that interest you.

In the fall migration period, look for waterfowl between Hennepin and Chillicothe or between Banner and Beardstown. Early in the morning and late in the afternoon you should see ducks flying over the river between their feeding and resting areas.

In winter, look for bald eagles on the lower part of the river at almost any spot having extensive areas of mature lowland woods nearby.

In spring and summer, look on branches overhanging the water for crested flycatchers, peewees, phoebes, and kingfishers. Look in the woods bordering the lower part of the river for pileated woodpeckers, redstarts, and prothonotary warblers. Watch the water ahead for purple martins, bank swallows, tree swallows, and rough-winged swallows. Look along high river banks for the homes of bank swallows. Look high overhead for the turkey vultures that nest on the cliffs between Florence (on U.S. Highway 36) and Grafton.

If you want to study geology, look for rock outcrops between Ottawa and Starved Rock and from Florence down to the mouth of the Illinois River and beyond.

If you have a special interest in prehistoric man, you can find mounds left by an ancient civilization at various places the length of the river. Stand and stare at the mounds if you wish, but leave the excavation to experts. Much valuable prehistoric material has been lost through the overenthusiastic digging of amateurs. A side trip to the Dickson Mounds between Havana and Lewistown will show you an unusually good sample of prehistoric man laid out before you by professional archeologists. The mounds are on a seldom-used road that runs west from Illinois Highway 97 and southeast from U.S. Highway 24. Road signs point the way.

If you want to become intimately acquainted with the Illinois River, with its currents, winds, and waves, see it as the French explorers saw it —from a canoe.

A canoe will allow you to see the river and its shoreline leisurely and at close range, to land on its islands, to explore the streams flowing into the river. It will give you a totally new view of the villages, cities, and farms along its shores.

Canoeing on the Illinois has some disadvantages. In a world of speedboats, it may seem tedious and tantalizingly slow. In some parts of the river and in some seasons it is dangerous. The Iroquois have gone from the Illinois, but not the speedboats, which can make life more than annoying for canoeists. Even the slow towboats leave a wake that can capsize a canoe operated by an unskilled modern voyageur.

The State Department of Conservation does not encourage canoeing on the Illinois. Instead, it has issued a booklet on canoeing possibilities of the Sangamon and other tributary streams, the Illinois and Michigan Canal west of Channahon, and the Illinois and Mississippi Canal (built between Bureau Junction and Rock Island too late to be of commercial use).

If, despite possible dangers, you decide to see the Illinois from a canoe, make sure you know how to handle your craft in rough water. Choose one or two companions who are at least as cautious and skilled as yourself. Then choose a time of year or part of the river in which you are least likely to encounter speedboats.

Middle or late October is ideal for a canoe trip on the Illinois. By that time a hard frost or a freeze should have sent speedboats and mosquitoes to cover. And Beardstown is a good place for launching the canoe.

Of course, you and your companions have provided yourselves with food, simple cooking utensils, and blankets or sleeping bags. Possibly you have a tent. Certainly you have life jackets, which you wear whenever you are on the water. If you do not insist on being primitive, you have a small motor at the stern of your canoe.

The river at Beardstown is now much wider and deeper than in the

Type of prehistoric mounds that can be seen along the Illinois River.

days Thomas Beard poled his ferry from one bank to the other. As you launch your canoe, the wind sweeps across the water and kicks up waves that threaten to swamp your craft.

You canoe down river under the highway bridge and pass Willow Island, which is within sight of Beardstown. At Towhead Island, close to Grape Island, you stop for lunch. As you are eating your last sandwich, you hear the muffled *chug chug* of a powerful diesel engine and through the openings between trees on Grape Island you catch glimpses of barges and a towboat gliding down river. The tow is scarcely visible in the distance as you resume your journey.

Trees line both shores of the river—most of them silver maples, willows, and cottonwoods. For several miles you see no cities, no villages, no houses even. Occasionally you glimpse the faded yellow of ripe cornstalks beyond the gray trunks and branches of trees that are losing their leaves in the October nights. Suddenly you see, rising above the treetops ahead of you, the upper part of a concrete grain elevator. As you round a bend in the river, the elevator comes into full view above the flatness of the surrounding landscape, like an ancient gray castle on a medieval plain.

Seen from the canoe, the elevator seems more closely related to the river than to the community that backs away from its base. For most of the year, it stands silent and alone at the edge of the water. But, at harvest time, farmers gather about it. They drive up to it in their red or green trucks filled to spilling over with bright yellow corn or dull yellow soybeans, empty their trucks, and stand about chatting before they drive away.

Red barges and green barges wait in the river at the base of the elevator. Grain pours out of a metal chute from the elevator into one of the barges—into one end of the barge first. Slowly the barge, moved along by an electric winch as the grain flows, settles in the water until less than half of it is visible. Later, perhaps after the visiting farmers have gone home to supper, the barge will be picked up by a towboat and started up river to Chicago or down river to St. Louis or Memphis or New Orleans.

At the La Grange Lock and Dam, a good-natured attendant opens the upper gates to let you and your canoe into the lock. You watch the sheer walls rise above you as the water falls. The lower gates swing open and you are again on your way down river.

Before nightfall, you begin looking for a campsite. Just above mile marker 75.9 you find one—an island in the river. Moore's Towhead, the navigation map calls it. High enough to be dry, it has a fairly large area free of poison ivy. It also has firewood, the trunks and branches of small trees that have been felled by the sharp teeth and strong jaws of beavers.

Before dark, you and your companions spread your sleeping bags on the ground. You have studied the sky. No rain tonight! You leave your tent rolled up.

As you crawl into your sleeping bag, you look up through the thinning foliage in a crisp October night at stars that in the dark blue sky seem brighter and more intensely white than you have ever seen them before. A large, bright star, you note, is at the end of a bare branch above you.

You close your eyes and doze. When you open them, you find that the bright star has moved from the end of the bare branch. You prop your eyelids open, not wanting to miss the moving of the star across the sky.

As you struggle to keep awake, you hear a gentle purring sound. Gradually the purring becomes louder, more distinct. A white glow lights the night sky far down river. The glow brightens and expands. The purring becomes a throb.

Suddenly the glow becomes two beams of white light, partly hidden until now by a bend in the tree-lined river. One of the beams of light

Grain elevators loading barges at Havana on the Illinois and, in the river, towboat with four barges.

plays on the water, shifts nervously to one of the banks and back to the water. The nervous light shifts to the island. Blinded, you roll over in your sleeping bag with your back to the light. Before you now, trunks and branches, washed in the white light, make a lacework pattern of silver against the black where the sky should be. So intense is the light that it blackens the dark blue of the night sky and extinguishes the stars.

The throb grows to a steady *chug, chug, chug.* Small lights, one red, one green, and several amber, outline dark angled shapes moving on the dark water. A *swish, swish* joins the *chug, chug, chug* as the dark shapes—barges—push through the water. At the end of the line of dark shapes is the towboat, its pilothouse dark, the doors and windows of its main deck rectangles of warm light. A man sits relaxed on a chair in an open doorway close to the water.

As barges and boat move farther up river, and darkness gathers them in, they are followed by the sound of waves from the wash kicked up by the engines, waves pounding against the island and the shore opposite, waves that pound, pound in the dark night.

The following day, after breakfast on the island, you continue your voyage down river. Above Meredosia, you see a clammer's boat drawn up on shore. It is a solitary reminder that, before the days of zippers and plastic, the making of buttons from clam shells was an important industry along the Illinois. You canoe under the highway bridge at Meredosia, past grain elevators, and on toward Naples, twenty-three miles by river from Beardstown.

You eat lunch in the warming noon sunlight on the sandy west shore where red leaves of a maple still cling to the branches. Across the river on the east shore, a grain elevator rises into a blue sky. Several yards down river from the elevator, a white building sits on a high bank that backs away from the water.

You head for the white building. As you near it, you see along the shore a weathered shed, a small wooden dock, a gasoline pump, a cabin cruiser beside the pump, and a sign, "THE BOATEL, NAPLES, ILL."

This is Naples, once the busiest port between St. Louis and Peoria!

In the white building, which is the principal part of the Boatel, you find Mr. and Mrs. Paul Vannier ready to provide fishermen and modern voyageurs with food and lodging and with abundant information about the past of a village that, like Chicago, had a disastrous fire but that, unlike Chicago, never recovered from it.

After you have telephoned a friend who has promised to pick up your canoe, your companions, and you, you look at the pictures on the west wall—pictures of steamboats that in years long gone regularly put in at Naples. You read the names of the boats and their years of service: *Prairie State*, 1850–1852; *Belle of Pike*, 1866–1872; *Calhoun*, 1876–1892; *D. H. Pike*, 1888–1898; *Golden Eagle*, 1904–1947. You read that the *Prairie State* exploded her boilers when racing the *Avalanche* near Pekin. You study the picture of the *Cotton Blossom*, a showboat that played to standing-room-only audiences at every regularly scheduled stop, and the picture of the dispatch boat, *Post Boy*, that during the Civil War was burned by Confederate spies. You read that the *Bald Eagle*, 1898–1934, twice a week, on Mondays and Thursdays, picked up as many as three hundred hogs at Naples or West Naples.

Steamboats, showboat, and hogs—all are reminders of the great days when the river was a vital part of the lives of the people who lived along its banks.

Index

ABOUT THE AUTHOR: Born in Wilmette, graduated from Northwestern University in Evanston, for many years technical editor of the Illinois Natural History Survey, and a resident of Urbana, James Ayars has long been acquainted with the State of Illinois and the Illinois River. In further preparation for writing *The Illinois River* Mr. Ayars took a trip on a towboat the entire length of the river and a shorter trip in a canoe as well as doing library research and gathering eyewitness accounts. The author of several other books for young readers both fiction and non-fiction, Mr. Ayars is the husband of the well-known author, Rebecca Caudill.

ABOUT THE ARTIST: Lili Réthi was born in Vienna and educated at the Academy of Art there. She came to New York City to live in 1939. Miss Réthi is well known for her drawings of industry and construction. Other special art interests include architecture, portrait and historical material. Her illustrations for *The Illinois River* reflect her fascination with the history of an area's development. She has illustrated sixty-three books to date. Miss Réthi has had numerous one-man exhibits in Europe and the United States. In 1961, she was elected a Fellow of the Royal Society of Arts in London in recognition of her work.

ABOUT THE BOOK: The text is set in Garamond. Display type is Perpetua with chapter numbers in Beton Open. Lili Réthi illustrated the book with pencil drawings, in which medium she gets a great range of values and textures.